C000263533

GCSE Additional Applied Science

1 Life care

Project directors Jenifer Burden
John Holman
Andrew Hunt
Robin Millar

Course editors Peter Campbell
Andrew Hunt

Module editor Ruth Holmes

Authors Ruth Holmes
Mike Kent
Merryn Kent

RECOGNISING ACHIEVEMENT

THE UNIVERSITY *of York*

OXFORD

Contents

Introduction

A very old man was overheard to say, 'If I knew I was going to live this long, I would have taken better care of myself . . .'

People are set to live increasingly long and healthy lives. But no matter how healthy our lifestyle, we will all suffer illness or injury at some time.

This module focuses on the people and organisations concerned with health and fitness. Life care professionals need to understand how the human body works, how to keep it in good condition, and how to help it mend when things go wrong.

Anna Bevan Storms to Victory

Two years ago Anna Bevan was an average runner. Last week she stormed to victory in the Commonwealth 800 metres, smashing the United Kingdom record. I asked coach Dan Forde about his winning partnership with Anna.

Dan, how did your partnership with Anna start?

I coach the athletics team at the university. Anna was studying sports science. During a physiology practical her maximal oxygen consumption (VO_2 max) was measured. She gave excellent results.

Her lecturer asked me to do a bleep test and step test on Anna. The tests confirmed that Anna was aerobically very fit. Anna had been an all-round sportsperson at school, playing tennis, netball, hockey, and rugby. However, her first love was athletics. She had tried sprinting but wasn't very successful. I offered to train Anna and she accepted.

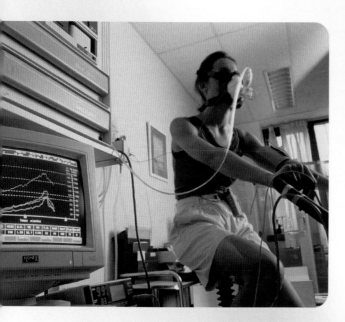

This is how Anna's aerobic fitness was tested. The equipment measures the maximum volume of oxygen she consumes in one minute as she cycles harder and harder. High values of oxygen consumption show high levels of endurance.

Did Anna begin training with you immediately?

No. First we spent some time talking and got to know each other. It's important for a coach and athlete to relate well and trust each other. Also, I had to check Anna's health before she started any training.

But surely the fitness test showed that Anna was healthy?

No, health and fitness are not the same thing. Although Anna performed well in fitness tests, she might have had a medical condition that made it dangerous for her to train seriously.

How did you check her health?

Anna completed a physical activity readiness questionnaire (PAR-Q). I also asked our athletics team doctor to carry out a more detailed health screening. If Anna was aiming to be an elite athlete, she would have to put her body under extreme physical stress.

What did the health check involve?

The doctor asked questions about Anna's lifestyle and medical history. Then came a series of of tests. He took blood and urine samples and measured her body temperature, resting heart rate, and blood pressure. Anna had an ECG to make sure her heart was healthy.

The doctor also measured Anna's weight and height to make a rough calculation of her body mass index. He took skinfold measurements to estimate her body fat content.

Were there any problems?

Anna was very healthy. However, her body mass index and skinfold measurements suggested her body fat content was a little high. It was not unhealthy, but not ideal for an elite athlete. I referred her to a sports nutritionist at the university who knows how foods and drinks affect sporting performance. The nutritionist gave Anna an eating plan that reduced her fat intake.

Once she had a clean bill of health, did Anna start training?

Well, not immediately. First I was curious to find out why Anna had not done well in school athletics competitions. I suspected that she might have been trying the wrong distance, so I asked for a muscle biopsy. The results showed that Anna's proportion of fast-twitch to slow-twitch fibres suited her to middle-distance events rather than to sprinting. Anna agreed to give this a try, and we designed a training programme for her.

What did the training programme involve?

Anna did sessions of several sprints with rest, walking, or light jogging in between. She also did one long, slow run each week. Before Anna trained each day her resting heart rate and body temperature were measured. She also weighed herself to make sure she was well hydrated. Water is lost during intensive exercise, and must be replaced before another intensive session.

Did everything go smoothly during the training programme?

Half-way through her first season Anna strained her hamstring muscle. The start of a race was delayed too long and she got cold. When she sprinted out of the blocks her muscle snapped, like an overstretched elastic band.

A physiotherapist was on hand to perform the RICE routine almost immediately. This reduced the damage. He also gave Anna a rehabilitation programme so she could run at full fitness again before the end of the season. Anna was able to complete her training programme and the rest, as they say, is history.

Recovery from a sports injury often involves RICE followed by stretching and strengthening exercises. RICE stands for Rest, Ice, Compression, and Elevation.

REST means immobilising the injured part (e.g. keeping the weight off a torn muscle).

ICE acts as an anaesthetic, reduces swelling, and slows the flow of blood to the injured area. To avoid damaging the tissue, the ice is applied indirectly (e.g. in a tea towel or plastic bag) for up to 20 minutes at a time with 30 minutes between applications.

COMPRESSION usually involves wrapping a bandage round the injured part to reduce swelling. The bandage should be snug but not too tight.

ELEVATION means raising the injured limb. This reduces swelling by helping to keep excess fluid away from the damaged area.

SIMPLE STRETCHING ROUTINES help to regain mobility, but only when swelling stops.

AEROBIC EXERCISING of the injured part is not restarted until it has regained at least 75% of the previous level of strength, and then only moderately. This exercise helps build muscle and return the athlete to peak fitness.

Accident and emergency

Life-saving professionals who handle accidents and emergencies must move quickly and confidently. They are trained to cope with a variety of situations.

Accident

At the ambulance station: an interview with paramedic Neil Hutchinson

What happens when you arrive at a road traffic accident?

First we check for hazards, so we can work safely without endangering the patient's life further.

How do you decide who to treat first?

We have a system called triage. This means deciding which patients need attention straight away, and which ones can safely wait until later. Patients with breathing or circulatory problems are treated first. We follow the ABC of first aid.

ABC?

A is for airways. We make sure they are open by tilting back the chin and looking for obstructions. Then we check breathing – that's B – giving mouth-to-mouth ventilation if necessary. C is for circulation. If a person has no heartbeat, we carry out cardiopulmonary resuscitation or CPR. If the person can't talk or is unconscious, we ask witnesses to tell us exactly what happened.

The police officer watches traffic so the paramedics can treat the casualty in safety. Witnesses can give vital information.

And then?

If there is no heartbeat we need to get the patient breathing, restore the heartbeat, give oxygen, and take them to hospital quickly. One paramedic continues with CPR while the other sets up the oxygen mask, the heart monitor, and the defibrillator. Sometimes we have to use a tube to keep the airways open. We put the person in the recovery position.

And time is of the essence?

Oh yes, it's critical. The first hour after injury is called the 'golden hour'. For example, I recently treated a man who came off his motorbike. His blood pressure was low which suggested internal bleeding. Thankfully, we got him to the operating theatre 45 minutes after the accident. So he was all right. The air ambulance speeds things up.

Who is treated next, after the ABC patients?

We assess those with major trauma, such as broken limbs or large wounds. Someone losing blood will be treated quickly to staunch the flow. Someone with a head injury might have dilated pupils or blood in the whites of their eyes, or their walking or speech may be affected.

What else might you have to do?

Well, some broken bones need to be treated straight away. A broken femur can be dangerous. The muscles in the thigh are so strong they tend to push the bone up into the abdomen. That's when you need traction.

And then it's to the hospital?

Yes. We deliver patients to the accident and emergency department. If we have radioed on ahead, a team is waiting to take over. We give the A&E staff details of any treatment we have given, and how the patient is.

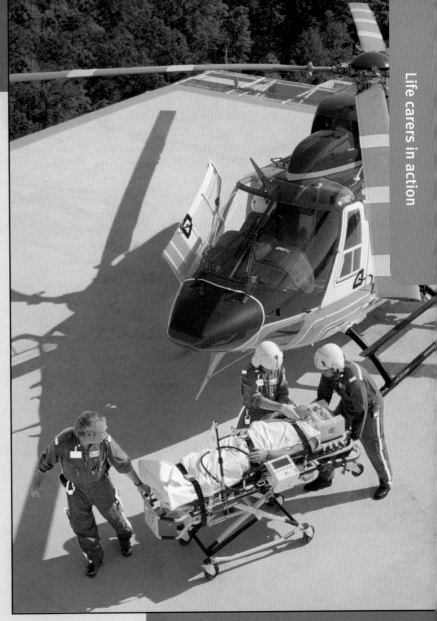

The air ambulance delivers the patient to hospital for immediate treatment.

Emergency: cardiac arrest

At the accident and emergency department: an interview with junior doctor Mike Yousif

What happens if a patient arrives at A&E with a suspected cardiac arrest?
We take details from the paramedics, and follow the ABC standard procedure.

Ah . . . I know all about that now. Airways, Breathing, and Circulation. But what next?
Once cardiac arrest is confirmed, we put a line into a blood vessel to give fluids or drugs. If the blood pressure is falling, we give fluids to maintain the blood pressure. After checking the airways, we use the defibrillator.

Mike Yousif at work in A&E at St Thomas's Hospital

That gives an electric shock?
Yes, that's right. We check the airways again and put in a tube to keep the airways open. A cycle of shocks and chest compressions is carried out, and we use an airbag to inflate the lungs. We do this three times.

If there's still no response, we give adrenaline. If the patient's heartbeat and breathing pattern is restored, we keep them in A&E until they are stable.

What problems might the patient have?
Heart failure or shock. We watch the heart monitor for signs of heart failure. We also monitor blood pressure closely.

Leaping into action with the defibrillator

Once the patient is stable, what happens next?
They are transferred to the cardiac care unit. If the condition remains serious, they will go to ITU – the intensive care unit.

On the cardiac care ward: an interview with staff nurse Jane Ratliff

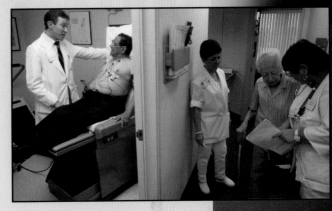

On the cardiac care ward

What happens when a patient arrives on the ward?

They stay on the heart monitor while we take details such as name, address, age, sex, next of kin, medication, and so on. We monitor vital signs and record them on a patient's chart. Once the doctor has seen the patient, we devise a care plan.

What exactly is a care plan?

It records how often we should take observations, and what medication to give. It also shows details of diet and fluids, and any proposed surgery.

What happens if the patient has another heart attack?

We bring the crash trolley which has a defibrillator, oxygen, and drugs. We carry out CPR.

And once the patient is recovering?

We continue checking the ECG trace on the heart monitor, along with temperature, pulse, breathing rate, and blood pressure. Once the patient has been stable for some hours, we will start a course of treatment. We tell the patient how to take the drugs and we monitor them for adverse reactions.

And when do you start planning for discharge?

As soon as possible. Hospital beds are in great demand. In some cases we arrange a meeting for the patient and anyone concerned with rehabilitation, such as a social worker, physiotherapist, occupational therapist, and any carers at home.

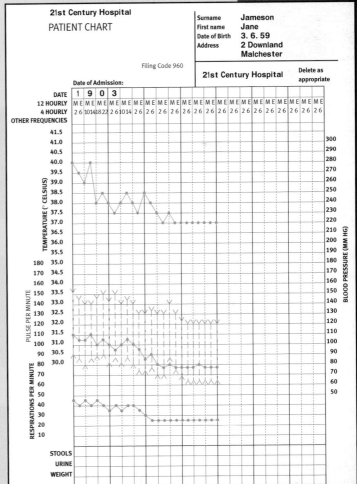

A patient's chart records temperature, blood pressure, pulse, and breathing rate. These must stabilise before the patient leaves the ward.

Antenatal care

Sandy Domoney is a midwife in Cornwall. She is based at a health centre, and also visits her patients at home.

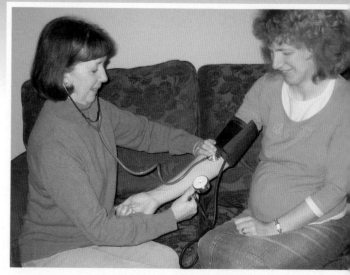

Sandy checks blood pressure at every appointment.

9 weeks

Finding out you're pregnant is a very exciting time. Most people do a home pregnancy test before contacting the health centre. The receptionist books the woman in to see me – often I'll visit at home for this first appointment. At this session I will give information and support so that she can make the right choices for her, and for the baby.

I give information on antenatal screening to test the fetus for several conditions, including Down's syndrome and spina bifida. The woman and her partner can then decide which tests to have.

With the woman's consent I take a blood sample to be tested for blood group, infections such as HIV, and immunity to rubella.

She will have about 10 antenatal appointments. The frequency depends on the individual's needs. She can also come to antenatal classes.

12 weeks

I arrange the first ultrasound scan and the results come back to me. I check to make sure the dates are correct. These pictures show how the baby develops – it's amazing how quickly they grow. You can see the baby's heart beating while the scan is being done. At the next appointment you can hear the heartbeat – a very positive experience.

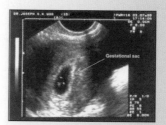

6 weeks

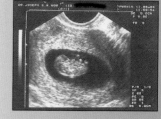

8 weeks

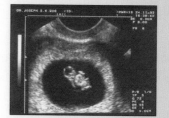

9 weeks

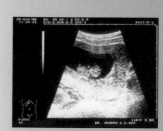

10 weeks

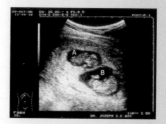

10 weeks – twins

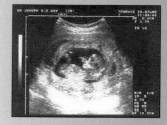

12 weeks

16 weeks

If the woman has decided to have screening for Down's syndrome and spina bifida, I take blood for this. I test urine for protein and sugar. Protein suggests possible infection, and sugar may show diabetes.

20 weeks

Another scan checks the baby for abnormalities. If there is concern about the position of the placenta, I'll offer another scan later in pregnancy. We can often tell now if it's a boy or a girl.

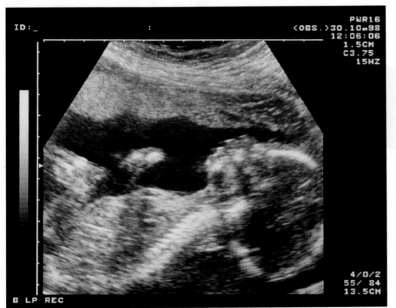

20 weeks

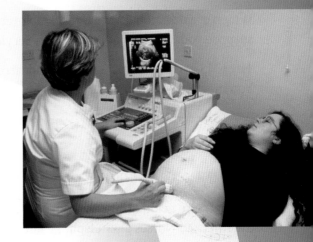

20–42 weeks

I see the woman regularly to check that the baby is growing well and that blood pressure and urine are normal. I complete a birth plan after 32 weeks saying whether she wants to have the baby at home or in hospital, and what sort of pain relief she would prefer.

41–42 weeks

If the baby has not been born we offer to start labour using artificial hormones. After 42 weeks the placenta starts to break down slightly. If this continues the baby could be at risk.

Labour and birth

The woman may have chosen to have the baby at home, looked after by my team. If she has chosen a hospital birth she is cared for by hospital midwives unless a problem arises. Then they call in the consultant.

Following birth

I visit the mother and baby at home for at least ten days to check that the baby is developing properly and the mother is well. It's lovely to see the parents with their new member of the family.

This section introduces some of the people and organisations involved in life care. Teams of skilled people work together to maintain and improve health and fitness. They respond to emergencies and provide treatment and aftercare for sick people.

Health and fitness organisations operate locally, nationally, and internationally. Their work is regulated to ensure high standards of service.

The National Health Service

About the NHS

Which organisation is the largest employer in Europe? The answer may surprise you. It's the National Health Service in England.

The NHS was set up in 1948 to provide free health care for everybody. You may meet NHS practitioners at

- the dentist's
- the optician's
- the local pharmacy
- the local health centre

You can also get help quickly from NHS Direct, by phone or on the Internet. Nurses give telephone advice about treatment or further help. The NHS Direct website has information about common illnesses and how to treat them.

The NHS employs over 1 million people. Of these, only about 430 000 are doctors, nurses, midwives or health visitors. The others have a wide variety of different jobs.

How did you become . . . a nurse?

You need a caring attitude to become a nurse. There are several routes to qualifying – the flow chart shows two common ones. You have to be at least $17\frac{1}{2}$ years old to start training.

five GSCEs (including English language and maths) → three-year diploma course

two A levels or equivalent → three- or four-year degree

common foundation programme – one year

specialise in:
- adult nursing
- children's nursing
- mental health nursing
- learning disability nursing

Nurses are helped by health care assistants. You need a good general education or work experience, and can gain NVQ qualifications on the job.

Doctors in the NHS

A **general practitioner (GP)** is your gateway to the NHS. Your local doctor can refer you to a hospital, arrange specialist treatment for you, and prescribe medicines.

But a GP is just one of a whole army of health care professionals. Together they aim to provide a high standard of health care for everyone.

The career of a doctor can take many paths. Instead of being a GP, doctors may specialise in a particular branch of medicine. A doctor's career might follow a path like this:

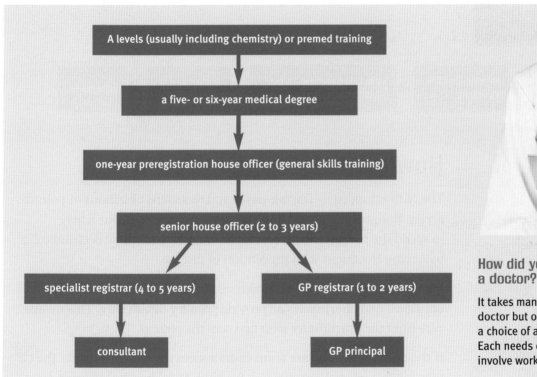

How did you become . . . a doctor?

It takes many years to become a doctor but once qualified there is a choice of about 60 specialities. Each needs different skills, but all involve working as part of a team.

Here are some of the specialist fields a doctor might choose:

- general practice (GP)
- paediatrics
- obstetrics and gynaecology
- pathology
- radiology
- anaesthetics
- ophthalmology
- surgery
- psychiatry
- cardiology

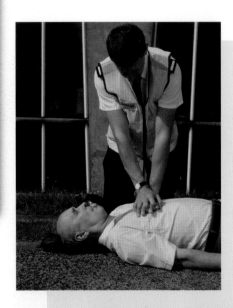

How did you become . . . a paramedic?

You have to be physically fit and highly skilled to be a paramedic. You have to make decisions quickly, use a variety of equipment, and be able to calm and reassure your patients.

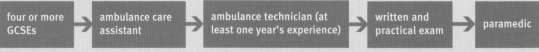

four or more GCSEs → ambulance care assistant → ambulance technician (at least one year's experience) → written and practical exam → paramedic

How the NHS is organised

The NHS is funded by the tax-payer and costs tens of billions of pounds a year. Budgets are limited and decisions are needed about where to spend the money. Health service managers make these decisions, balancing treatment with prevention of disease.

Paramedics, GPs, midwives, health visitors, practice nurses, dentists, opticians, and pharmacies all provide **primary health care**. This means care from the practitioner who first sees the patient.

If the primary health care team cannot meet the patient's needs, the GP may make a **referral**, usually to a hospital. Local hospitals cannot treat every condition, and some hospitals provide specialised care. Two famous hospitals in Britain are Stoke Mandeville Hospital, specialising in spinal injuries, and Great Ormond Street Hospital for Children.

As well as specialist hospital treatment, national health care has many other branches. Two examples are providing blood and protecting public health.

The National Blood Service

The National Blood Service is a branch of the NHS that delivers blood and blood products to anywhere in England and North Wales. The service also

- carries out research
- offers clinical support to hospitals
- educates and trains people who use transfusion machines

Features of a national health service

- provides health care for everybody
- provides specialist care that is not always available locally
- monitors national trends
- plans suitable health care
- decides where and when resources should be used
- balances providing direct health care with organising and managing the service

Key words

general practitioner (GP)
primary health care
referral

The Health Protection Agency

The Health Protection Agency is an independent health authority within the NHS. It was set up to protect public health and reduce the impact of

- infectious diseases
- chemical hazards
- poisons
- radiation hazards

The Health Protection Agency constantly monitors these threats to public health. It informs the Government about particular dangers, such as the spread of an infectious disease, and advises on the best action.

The Agency also promotes health education and public information. It studies health trends and lifestyle changes in the population. Public information campaigns can then be targeted at particular problems it has found. These campaigns are expensive, but they can save lives. They also save money in the long run, as less has to be spent on treatment.

One campaign was about chlamydia, the most common sexually transmitted infection in the UK. If untreated it can cause serious complications, particularly in women. But people cannot always tell they have the disease. So it's easy to pass it on to someone else without knowing.

A pregnant woman can pass the infection on to her baby during birth. The baby may have an eye infection or pneumonia.

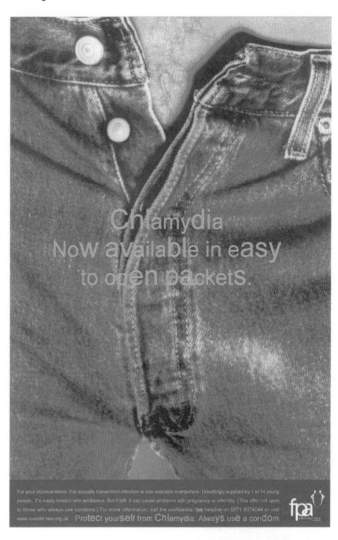

If untreated, chlamydia can cause serious health problems. The Government launched this health education campaign to raise awareness of this sexually transmitted disease.

Questions

1 Give two characteristics of a national health service.

2 Give one advantage and one disadvantage of contacting NHS Direct instead of visiting the GP when you feel unwell.

3 Name three different providers of primary health care.

4 Name two fields you could specialise in if you became
   a a doctor
   b a nurse
   c a health care assistant

The World Health Organization

The World Health Organization (WHO) is the United Nations agency for health. WHO coordinates health information from around the world. This makes it easier to combat disease in each country, and also makes life safer for travellers.

WHO responds to global health problems such as

- the world epidemic of HIV/AIDS
- the Asian earthquake and tsunami in December 2004

WHO and HIV/AIDS

HIV is a sexually transmitted virus. People with HIV may go on to develop AIDS. With this disease the body's immune system is weakened. Treatments are being developed but many people die of AIDS.

WHO estimates that 40 million people in the world are HIV positive. In 2003, about 5 million people were newly infected and 3 million people died of AIDS.

WHO tries to make sure that AIDS sufferers have equal access to treatment. The agency also helps organise media campaigns to educate people about AIDS worldwide.

The Asian tsunami

Following the earthquake and tsunami, WHO worked to

- coordinate the transport of resources to where they were most needed
- track the spread of diseases and advise on their treatment
- make sure everyone had equal access to health care
- advise about public health problems such as water quality

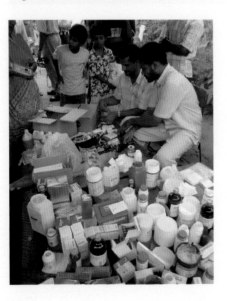

Aid for tsunami victims had to be organised and coordinated.

Promoting a healthy lifestyle

In the UK two major causes of premature death are **cancer** and **coronary heart disease**. It has been estimated that coronary heart disease alone costs the UK economy £10 million a year.

Another growing problem is obesity, particularly in children. Young people today are becoming less active and the problem is made worse by the popularity of high-fat convenience foods.

People's chances of suffering from coronary heart disease, some cancers, and obesity are affected by their lifestyle. Health education campaigners try to encourage people to

- eat more healthily
- exercise more
- drink less
- stop smoking

Many organisations work to encourage people to follow a healthy lifestyle, for example

- The British Heart Foundation (BHF) provides support and information for heart patients and their families. It funds research into heart disease and educates the public and health professionals about heart issues.
- The Food Standards Agency (FSA) is an independent body that helps make sure our food in Britain is safe, healthy, and fairly marketed.
- The Food Advertising Unit (FAU) is a centre for information, communication, and research in the area of food advertising, particularly TV advertising to children.

The UK has one of the highest rates of death from coronary heart disease in the world. A poor diet, high in saturated fats, may contribute to this. Over 120 000 UK deaths a year are caused by CHD.

Key words

cancer
coronary heart disease

Questions

1 List three health problems that may be associated with lifestyle choices people make.

2 Why do you think it is important to monitor and research the effect of food advertising on children?

Fitness and leisure in health

Improving health though sport and exercise

Regular sport and exercise have many health benefits. Sport has a social role in communities. Sport and exercise also play an important part in **rehabilitation** after illness.

Local authorities provide facilities for sport and recreation in the community, such as sports and leisure centres and playing fields. They have to balance the need for sports amenities with the need to control local taxes. Sports clubs and privately run gyms and health centres also provide facilities for sport.

Fitness instructors and health

Under the Exercise Referral Scheme, doctors can refer patients to exercise programmes supervised by fitness instructors at local gyms and leisure centres. The scheme is intended for a wide range of patients including those with coronary heart disease, obesity, mental health problems, and patients rehabilitating after falls or accidents.

Key words
rehabilitation

How did you become . . . a fitness instructor?

Fitness instructors have to work hard, often at unsocial hours, for low initial pay.

To be a fitness instructor you should have a minimum of NVQ level 2 in coaching, teaching, and instructing exercise and fitness. You should also join the Register of Exercise Professionals. This requires instructors to work within a code of ethical practice. It includes a category for instructors on the Exercise Referral Scheme.

How did you become . . . a coach?

A good coach is enthusiastic, cares about people, and can communicate well.

Each sport has a national governing body with its own coaching qualifications. You must have one of these qualifications to coach in that sport. Although there are many jobs available for qualified coaches, most coaches are part-time or voluntary.

The Fitness Industry Association (FIA) has a code of practice that sets standards for its member health and gym clubs. With the Government, the FIA has also developed a list of fitness professionals that are qualified, along with a list of the clubs which employ them.

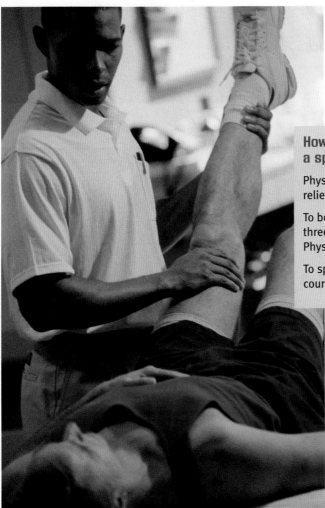

Physiotherapy

If you are injured as a result of sport or exercise you might visit a sports physiotherapist. These specialist physiotherapists are trained to return you to full fitness as quickly, but as safely, as possible.

How did you become . . . a sports physiotherapist?

Physiotherapists use physical methods to treat injury, and to prevent and relieve pain. The work is quite strenuous.

To become a physiotherapist you need five GCSEs including two sciences, three A levels, a relevant degree, and you need to become a Chartered Physiotherapist.

To specialise as a sports physiotherapist you do a special postgraduate course. You also need practical experience.

Questions

1 What qualifications do you need to be a fitness instructor?

2 How does giving people access to local sports facilities support the aims of a national health service?

3 Name an independent organisation that cooperates with the Government to improve health through sport.

Healthy lifestyle guidelines

Take more exercise

To improve health and fitness, people should take **aerobic exercise** that increases the heart rate. They should exercise for at least 15 minutes, three times a week. Examples include riding a bicycle, walking to school or college, jogging, playing football, aerobics, dance classes, skateboarding, and many more. Sport and exercise help

- reduce body fat
- strengthen bones
- improve coordination, balance, and flexibility
- improve stamina and concentration
- fight depression and anxiety

Eat five portions of fruit and vegetables a day

Fresh fruit and vegetables contain important minerals and vitamins. These improve general health. **Antioxidants** may help to prevent cancer.

Fruit and vegetables are also an important source of fibre in the diet, reducing the risk of diseases of the gut.

Eat less saturated fat

Many 'fast foods' contain high levels of saturated fat and cholesterol (a white waxy substance). These may increase the risk of **coronary heart disease**. Cholesterol can build up in the arteries, making them narrower or even blocking them. If the coronary artery becomes blocked, a heart attack may result.

Eat less salt

High levels of salt in the diet can cause a raised blood pressure, which in turn can lead to heart disease.

Eat less sugar

A diet high in sugar can cause tooth decay. Most sugary foods are also energy rich. Consuming more energy than you need leads to an increase in body weight.

People who are 30% overweight are said to be **obese**. Obesity puts an increased strain on the heart, and increases blood pressure. It can cause **diabetes** and damage to the joints.

Do not smoke

Smoking causes lung diseases such as lung cancer, bronchitis, and **emphysema**. Smoking also causes narrowing of the arteries. This leads to high blood pressure and an increased risk of coronary heart disease.

Do not get involved with drugs

Many substances, both legal and illegal, can be bad for the body. Drugs have to be broken down by the liver or passed out in the urine by the kidneys, so drug abuse can damage the liver and kidneys.

Drug abuse can also cause alterations in the brain, leading to dependency and depression, and changes in behaviour.

Do not drink alcohol in excess

Drinking too much can lead to

- alcoholism
- liver damage
- increased aggression and violence
- cancers of the liver, oesophagus, and mouth
- increased risk of **stroke** (a blood clot forming in a blood vessel in the brain)

For an adult female, drinking more than 14 units per week is bad for her health. Adult males should drink no more than 21 units per week.

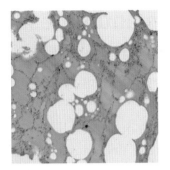
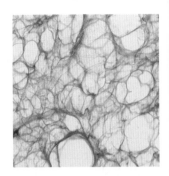

Detail of a lung from a person suffering from emphysema (left) and a healthy lung (right). In emphysema the alveoli break down, greatly reducing the surface area for gas exchange. Emphysema is caused by smoking.

A unit of alcohol is 10 cm^3 of pure alcohol. Counting units of alcohol can help us keep track of the amount we're drinking.

pint of ordinary strength lager — 2 units
pint of strong lager — 3 units
pint of bitter — 2 units
pint of ordinary strength cider — 2 units
175 cm^3 glass of red or white wine — 2 units
pub measure of spirits — 1 unit
alcopop — 1.5 units

Questions

1 Explain in your own words why it is sensible to

  a eat five portions of fruit and vegetables a day

  b have a low intake of salt

  c drink only moderate amounts of alcohol

  d not smoke

  e take regular aerobic exercise

2 A woman drank 4 half pints of strong lager, 5 large (175 cm^3) glasses of red wine, and 4 measures of brandy in a week.

  a How many units was this?

  b What advice would you give her?

Key words

aerobic exercise

antioxidants

coronary heart disease

obese

diabetes

emphysema

stroke

Assessing health and fitness

Blood pressure and pulse rate

A normal value for blood pressure is about 120/80 mm Hg. A raised blood pressure can be a sign of kidney, heart, or circulatory disease.

A normal resting pulse rate is about 60–100 beats per minute. The pulse rate may be raised during exercise, or because of a health problem. A weak pulse rate may be a sign of low blood pressure, or a heart disorder.

Regular exercise lowers the pulse rate, and also helps lower the blood pressure.

An **electrocardiogram (ECG)** shows the electrical changes in the heart as it beats. ECGs also show any abnormalities in the heartbeat.

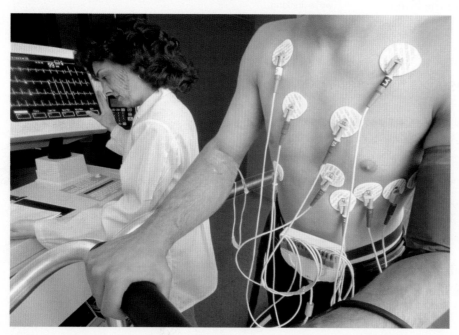

To take an ECG, electrodes are placed on the chest and limbs. The screen shows how the heart responds as the subject exercises.

Measuring body fat: BMI and skinfold measurements

The **body mass index (BMI)** is a calculation to show whether someone is underweight, overweight, or at a desirable weight. BMIs are used to produce health guidelines. However, BMI tables assume that everyone with a high BMI has a high level of body fat and is therefore unhealthy. This may not always be true – for example, body-builders with very large muscles may have a high BMI but a low body fat content.

Folds in the skin are thicker when there is more fat in the body. **Skinfold measurements** are another method used to estimate the level of body fat.

Measuring physical activity level

Daily exercise is good for you, but we need to measure how much exercise people do each day. The **physical activity level (PAL)** is a way of calculating this. It depends on the **metabolic rate**, the rate at which the body uses energy.

$$PAL = \frac{\text{total energy required over 24 hours}}{\text{basal metabolic rate over 24 hours}}$$

The World Health Organization recommends a PAL of at least 1.7 for cardiovascular fitness. The higher the PAL, the more exercise is done a day.

Calculating the total energy required over 24 hours

This involves

  ▶ recording all the different activities carried out in 24 hours, and for how long (for example, playing football for 40 minutes, . . .)

  ▶ looking up how much energy per hour these activities use (for example, football uses 550 kcal per hour for a 70 kg person)

  ▶ calculating the total energy used for all the activities in 24 hours

Calculating the basal metabolic rate

The **basal metabolic rate (BMR)** is the rate at which the body uses energy at complete rest. It is different for different people. This is how BMR is calculated:

For males
$66.67 + (13.75 \times \text{weight in kg}) + (5 \times \text{height in cm}) - (6.76 \times \text{age in years})$

For females
$665.1 + (9.56 \times \text{weight in kg}) + (1.85 \times \text{height in cm}) - (4.68 \times \text{age in years})$

Examples

Mike is 52, weighs 68 kg, and is 165 cm tall.

Mike's BMR is
$66.67 + (13.75 \times 68) + (5 \times 165) - (6.76 \times 52) = 1475$

Mike calculated that he used 2000 kcal of energy over 24 hours.

Mike's PAL is $\frac{2000}{1475} = 1.36$

Bimla is 43, weighs 50 kg, and is 150 cm tall.

Bimla's BMR is
$665.1 + (9.56 \times 50) + (1.85 \times 150) - (4.68 \times 43) = 1219$

Bimla calculated that she used 2100 kcal of energy over 24 hours.

Bimla's PAL is $\frac{2100}{1219} = 1.72$

Questions

1 What is the purpose of
   a ECG   **b** BMI   **c** skinfold measurements   **d** PAL?

2 Why might skinfold measurements give a better estimate of body fat content than the BMI?

3 Look at the examples. Do Mike's and Bimla's PAL levels show that they do enough exercise?

Key words

electrocardiogram (ECG)
body mass index (BMI)
skinfold measurements
physical activity level (PAL)
metabolic rate
basal metabolic rate (BMR)

The respiratory system

All human cells carry out **respiration** to provide them with energy. They need oxygen for respiration, and the process produces carbon dioxide.

The **respiratory system** is the organ system that supplies oxygen to the body, and removes carbon dioxide. This swapping of oxygen for carbon dioxide is called **gas exchange**. The **lungs** are the site of gas exchange, and here the gases move between the air and the blood.

The airways

The **airways** are a system of tubes carrying air deep into the lungs.

Key words

respiration
respiratory system
gas exchange
lungs
airways
trachea
bronchus (bronchi)
bronchiole
alveolus (alveoli)

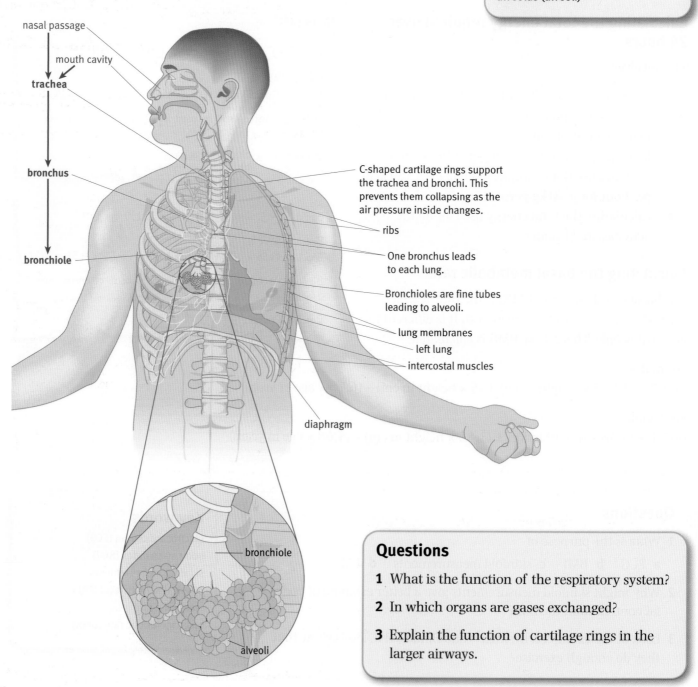

nasal passage

mouth cavity

trachea

bronchus

bronchiole

C-shaped cartilage rings support the trachea and bronchi. This prevents them collapsing as the air pressure inside changes.

ribs

One bronchus leads to each lung.

Bronchioles are fine tubes leading to alveoli.

lung membranes

left lung

intercostal muscles

diaphragm

bronchiole

alveoli

Questions

1 What is the function of the respiratory system?

2 In which organs are gases exchanged?

3 Explain the function of cartilage rings in the larger airways.

Gas exchange in the alveoli

Gas exchange takes place in the **alveoli**. These are tiny air sacs surrounded by fine blood capillaries.

> Oxygen passes from the air in the alveoli into the blood.
> Carbon dioxide passes from the blood into the air.

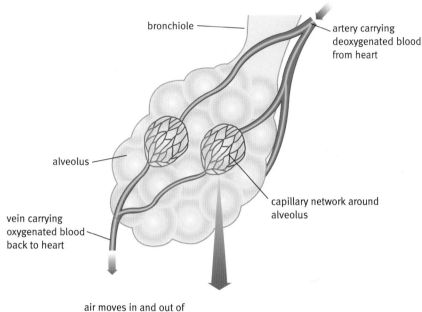

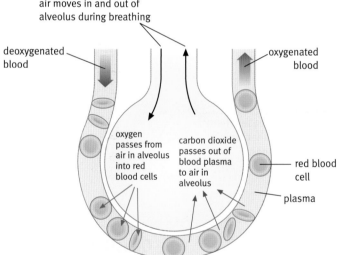

The circulatory system then carries the oxygen to all the body cells for respiration. It collects their carbon dioxide.

The alveoli and capillaries are well suited to their function of gas exchange:

> There are many millions of alveoli, together making a huge area for gas exchange.
> The walls of both the alveoli and the blood capillaries are very thin. This makes the distance between the air in the lungs and the blood very small.

Questions

1 In which direction do the following gases move in the alveoli, air to blood or blood to air?

   a carbon dioxide
   b oxygen

2 Describe the path of a molecule of oxygen from the air entering the nose, through the airways, and into the blood. List the structures it passes through.

3 List three ways in which the gas exchange system is adapted to its function.

Ventilating the lungs

Blood continually flows through the capillaries surrounding the alveoli, carrying away oxygen and bringing new carbon dioxide to the lungs. The air in the alveoli is also constantly replaced, supplying new oxygen and removing carbon dioxide.

The air is replaced by breathing or **ventilation**. This is the rhythmic movement of the lungs, taking air in (inhalation) and pushing it out (exhalation).

Breathing in – inhalation

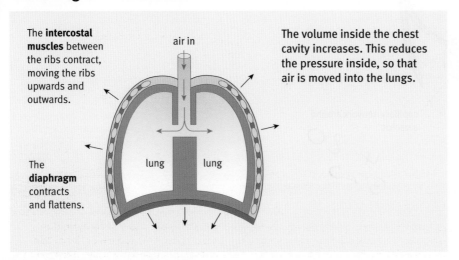

The **intercostal muscles** between the ribs contract, moving the ribs upwards and outwards.

air in

The volume inside the chest cavity increases. This reduces the pressure inside, so that air is moved into the lungs.

The **diaphragm** contracts and flattens.

lung   lung

Breathing out – exhalation

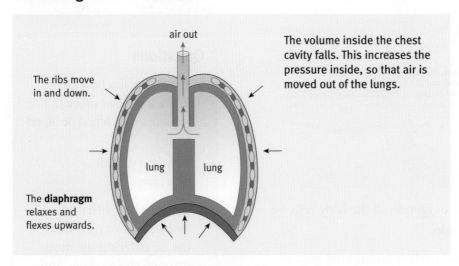

air out

The ribs move in and down.

The volume inside the chest cavity falls. This increases the pressure inside, so that air is moved out of the lungs.

lung   lung

The **diaphragm** relaxes and flexes upwards.

One complete breath is an inhalation, an exhalation, and a pause. The **breathing rate** is the number of complete breaths in one minute.

At rest, most people breathe 16–18 times a minute. During exercise breathing becomes deeper and faster.

Key words

ventilation
intercostal muscles
diaphragm
breathing rate

Questions

1 Explain in your own words how the lungs are inflated and deflated.

2 Describe the effect on gas exchange if ventilation stopped. How would the air in the alveoli be different?

3 Why does the breathing rate need to increase during exercise?

The cardiovascular system

The **cardiovascular system** carries substances around the body. It has three parts:

- blood vessels
- the heart
- blood

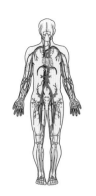

Key words

cardiovascular system
artery
capillary
vein

Blood vessels

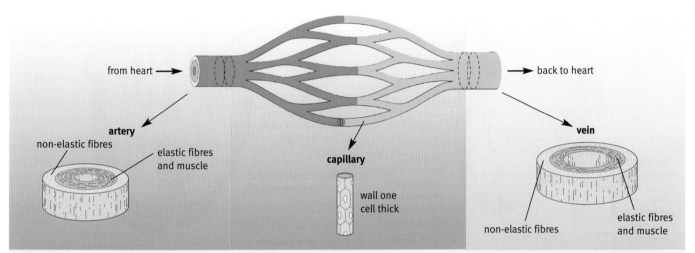

from heart →

artery
non-elastic fibres
elastic fibres and muscle

capillary
wall one cell thick

→ back to heart

vein
non-elastic fibres
elastic fibres and muscle

Arteries carry blood away from the heart. They have thick muscular walls to cope with the high pressure of blood as it leaves the heart. Arteries divide into **capillaries**.

Capillaries branch and spread through the body taking blood to every cell. The walls are very thin and leaky. Plasma carrying oxygen, food, carbon dioxide, and water can pass out to the cells. Capillaries join up to form **veins**.

Veins carry blood back to the heart. They have thinner walls so are wider inside than arteries. Blood pressure is low. When you move around, your body muscles help push the blood along veins. Veins have valves to stop the blood flowing backwards.

The blood vessels form a continuous system around the body. They carry blood through the heart twice on each complete trip round the body. Blood goes:

- to the lungs to pick up oxygen
- back to the heart for a pressure boost
- around the body to deliver oxygen
- back to the heart

and then the whole cycle repeats.

Questions

1 Make a table to compare the three types of blood vessel.

2 Why do arteries have thicker walls than veins?

3 The human circulation is called a double circulation. Why do you think this is?

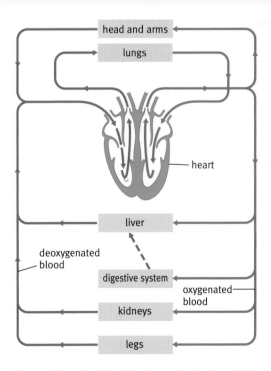

head and arms
lungs
heart
liver
deoxygenated blood
digestive system
oxygenated blood
kidneys
legs

The total length of the blood vessels is about 150 000 km. End to end they would stretch 2½ times around the world.

The heart

The circulation of blood is pumped by the heart. The heart beats automatically but the rate varies with the body's level of stress and exertion.

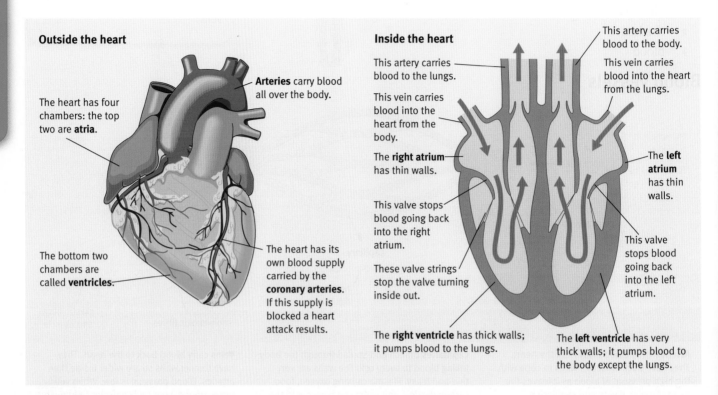

Outside the heart

Arteries carry blood all over the body.

The heart has four chambers: the top two are **atria**.

The bottom two chambers are called **ventricles**.

The heart has its own blood supply carried by the **coronary arteries**. If this supply is blocked a heart attack results.

Inside the heart

This artery carries blood to the lungs.

This vein carries blood into the heart from the body.

The **right atrium** has thin walls.

This valve stops blood going back into the right atrium.

These valve strings stop the valve turning inside out.

The **right ventricle** has thick walls; it pumps blood to the lungs.

This artery carries blood to the body.

This vein carries blood into the heart from the lungs.

The **left atrium** has thin walls.

This valve stops blood going back into the left atrium.

The **left ventricle** has very thick walls; it pumps blood to the body except the lungs.

Blood pressure and pulse

The **blood pressure** is the force of blood per unit area as it flows through the blood vessels.

▶ The **systolic blood pressure** is the highest pressure, when the left ventricle contracts to pump blood into the arteries.

▶ The **diastolic blood pressure** is lower. It is the pressure in the arteries when the heart is relaxed and filling with blood.

As the left ventricle contracts, surges in blood pressure cause the arteries to expand and contract. This can be felt as a **pulse** in the major arteries.

Questions

1 Compare the cross-section of the heart here with the circulation diagram on page 27. Describe the path of the blood into and out of

   a the right side of the heart **b** the left side of the heart

2 What are the two readings quoted for blood pressure? Explain the difference between them.

Key words

atrium (atria)
ventricle
coronary arteries
blood pressure
systolic blood pressure
diastolic blood pressure
pulse

Blood

You have 5–7 litres of blood circulating round your body.
Blood

- carries oxygen and nutrients to all your tissues
- removes wastes such as carbon dioxide and urea
- transports hormones
- helps to regulate the body's temperature and water content

A microscope reveals the structure of blood.

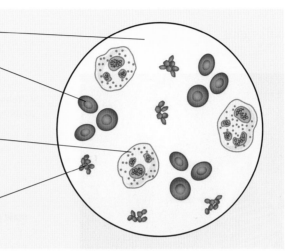

Plasma: a pale yellow watery fluid containing nutrients, hormones, and proteins.

Red blood cells contain the red pigment **haemoglobin** that carries oxygen. Their biconcave shape increases the surface area, making gas exchange more efficient. They have no nucleus, to make more space for haemoglobin.

White blood cells are of various shapes and have a nucleus. They defend the body against infection. You have more white blood cells in your blood when you have an infection.

Platelets: small fragments of cells involved in blood clotting. Clotting is important in stopping the flow of blood after an injury.

Problems with blood

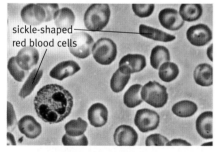

sickle-shaped red blood cells

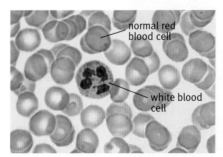

normal red blood cell

white blood cell

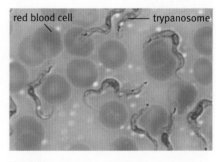

red blood cell — trypanosome

These photomicrographs show the difference between the red blood cells of a person with **sickle-cell anaemia** (left), and those of a healthy person (middle).

The microscope reveals trypanosomes. Trypanosomes are single-celled organisms that live some of their life cycle in the blood of vertebrates, including humans. Trypanosomes that cause sleeping sickness are common in parts of Africa. They are transmitted by the bite of a tsetse fly.

Questions

1 Name two substances that are transported around the body in blood.

2 How do red blood cells and white blood cells differ in

   a their appearance   **b** their function?

Key words

plasma
red blood cells
haemoglobin
white blood cells
platelets
sickle-cell anaemia

The skeleton

Your **skeleton** provides a tough, flexible framework for the rest of your body. Without it you would be a jellyfish-like mass.

As well as supporting your body your skeleton:

- stores minerals such as calcium and phosphorus
- makes red blood cells, platelets, and some white blood cells in bone marrow
- forms a system of levers with muscles attached, enabling the body to move
- protects internal organs

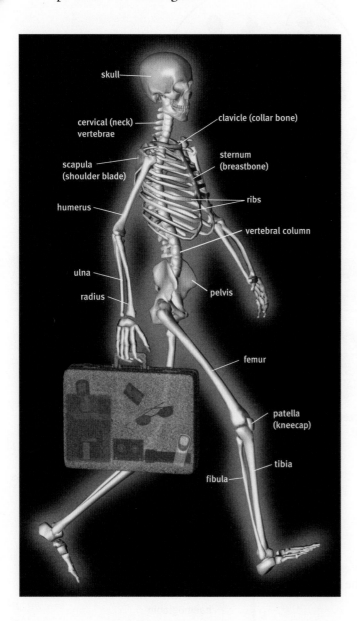

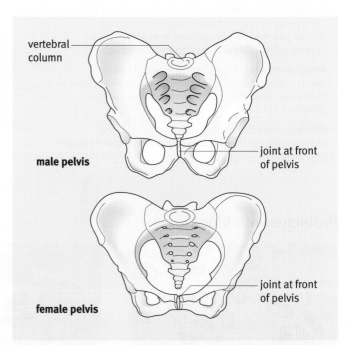

The pelvis protects the reproductive organs. The female pelvis is shallower and wider for childbearing. During the later stages of pregnancy a fibrous joint at the front of the pelvis loosens to allow it to become even wider.

Questions

1 List four functions of the skeleton.

2 What features in the diagram on the opposite page show that bone is living tissue?

3 How does exercise change bones?

Key word

skeleton

Living bone

The skeleton is not just dry bone. Its tissues, bone and cartilage, are made of living cells. They are moist and highly active. Blood brings nutrients and oxygen to the living cells. Bone is continually broken down and rebuilt.

Even an adult's skeleton is constantly changing. Weight-bearing exercises such as jogging stimulate bone growth, increasing its density. Inactivity can make bone less dense and weaker.

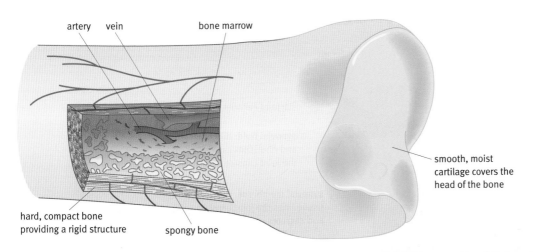

artery　vein　bone marrow

smooth, moist cartilage covers the head of the bone

hard, compact bone providing a rigid structure　spongy bone

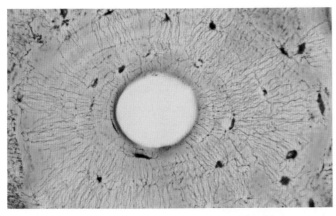

A Light micrograph of bone (×600). You can see the central canal surrounded by circular bands. The dark dots are cavities containing bone cells.

B An electron micrograph is taken using a beam of electrons instead of light. This allows more detail to be seen. This transmission electron micrograph shows a thin section through one cavity and its bone cell (×4000).

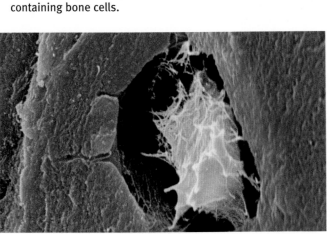

C A scanning electron micrograph shows details of the surface of the sample. This shows a single bone cell in its cavity (×4000).

31

Joints, muscles, and movement

Two or more bones meet at a **joint**.

Different types of joint allow different sorts of movement.

Most joints in the body are synovial joints. The knee is the largest synovial joint.

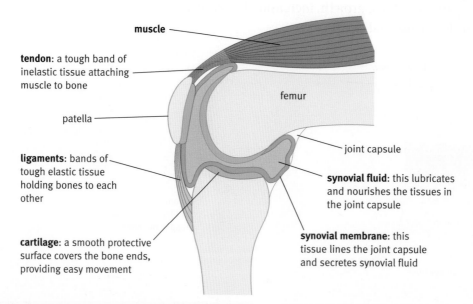

- **muscle**
- **tendon:** a tough band of inelastic tissue attaching muscle to bone
- patella
- **ligaments:** bands of tough elastic tissue holding bones to each other
- **cartilage:** a smooth protective surface covers the bone ends, providing easy movement
- femur
- joint capsule
- **synovial fluid:** this lubricates and nourishes the tissues in the joint capsule
- **synovial membrane:** this tissue lines the joint capsule and secretes synovial fluid

Taking a muscle biopsy

A muscle biopsy is a procedure to remove and examine a piece of muscle tissue. With athletes, they show the relative proportions of two types of muscle fibre, slow-twitch fibres and fast-twitch fibres.

Slow-twitch fibres

- have a very good blood supply
- contract slowly
- fatigue slowly
- need a good supply of oxygen

In contrast, fast-twitch fibres

- have a poor blood supply
- contract quickly and powerfully
- can function briefly without oxygen
- fatigue quickly

People with a high proportion of slow-twitch fibres are better adapted to endurance sports such as the marathon. Those with more fast-twitch fibres are better adapted to sprinting.

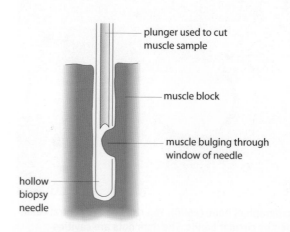

- plunger used to cut muscle sample
- muscle block
- muscle bulging through window of needle
- hollow biopsy needle

A muscle biopsy needle

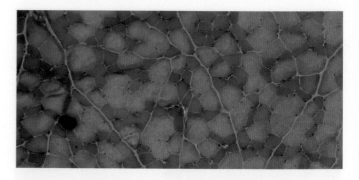

This photomicrograph of a thin slice of human muscle shows fast-twitch fibres (light) and slow-twitch fibres (dark).

How muscles move bones

A muscle contracts to pull on a bone and move it at a joint. **Skeletal muscles** can be moved at will.

Muscles cannot push, they can only pull. After contracting they are only stretched again when the bone is pulled back by another muscle. So at least two muscles act at each joint:

- one contracts to bend the joint
- the other contracts to straighten it

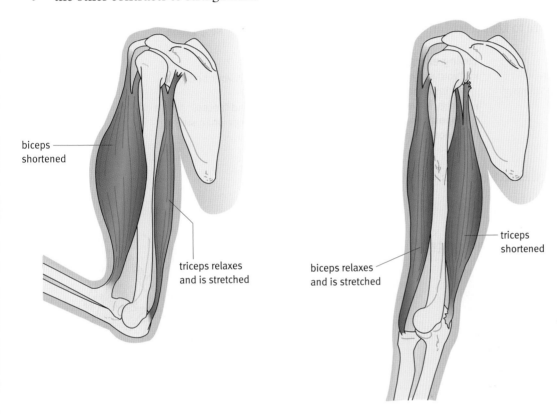

The biceps contracts to bend the arm; the triceps contracts to straighten it.

There are over 600 muscles attached to the human skeleton. They make up almost half the total body weight.

Questions

1 What is the difference between a tendon and a ligament?

2 Name the parts of a synovial joint and explain their functions.

3 Name the muscle whose action

   a bends the arm

   b straightens the arm

Key words

joint
muscle
tendon
ligament
cartilage
synovial fluid
synovial membrane
skeletal muscle

33

Control of body temperature

A constant body temperature

Energy is transferred from warmer objects to cooler ones. The bigger the temperature difference the greater the rate of cooling.

The **body core temperature** is the temperature of the internal vital organs. Humans keep their body core temperature constant at around 37 °C no matter how warm or cold their surroundings.

The skin and the temperature regulatory centre in the brain continually adjust the body temperature to keep it within a narrow range.

glucose + oxygen

carbon dioxide + water + ENERGY

Respiration

Gaining energy ⇑

▸ **Respiration** warms your body.
▸ On a hot sunny day the Sun warms your body.

Losing energy ⇓

▸ If your surroundings are cooler than your body, your body will lose energy to the surroundings.
▸ Energy leaves your body in your warm urine and faeces.
▸ **Evaporation** causes energy loss. You lose energy when sweat evaporates and in the moist air you breathe out.

Respiration releases energy. Exercise makes you hot because of respiration in muscle cells.

The skin and temperature control

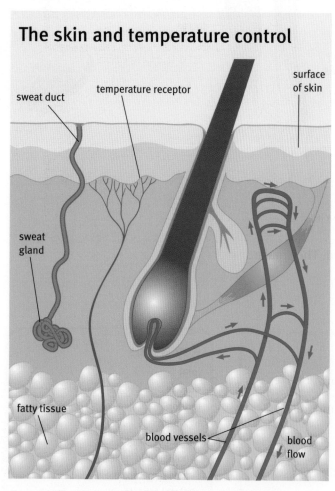

sweat duct

temperature receptor

surface of skin

sweat gland

fatty tissue

blood vessels

blood flow

Cross-section through the skin. The layer of fatty tissue insulates the body and limits energy loss to the surroundings.

Sweating . . .

When you are hot you **sweat**. Water evaporates from your skin, transferring energy away from you.

. . . and shivering

When you are cold you **shiver**. Your muscles contract, and this generates energy to help you warm up. Exercise such as running around or beating your arms has the same effect.

Key words

body core temperature
respiration
evaporation
sweating
shivering

The body's response to changes in air temperature

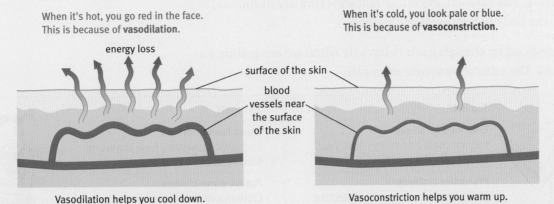

When it's hot, you go red in the face. This is because of **vasodilation**.

When it's cold, you look pale or blue. This is because of **vasoconstriction**.

energy loss

surface of the skin

blood vessels near the surface of the skin

Vasodilation helps you cool down.

The blood vessels near the skin surface get fatter (dilate). This diverts blood closer to the surface. Energy is transferred through the skin to the cooler air.

Vasoconstriction helps you warm up.

The blood vessels near the skin surface get narrower (constrict), so less blood flows through them. Less energy is transferred through the skin to the cooler air.

The control of body temperature

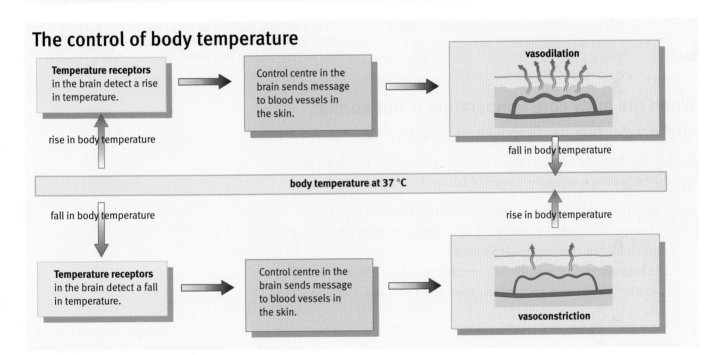

Temperature receptors in the brain detect a rise in temperature.

Control centre in the brain sends message to blood vessels in the skin.

vasodilation

rise in body temperature

fall in body temperature

body temperature at 37 °C

fall in body temperature

rise in body temperature

Temperature receptors in the brain detect a fall in temperature.

Control centre in the brain sends message to blood vessels in the skin.

vasoconstriction

Questions

1 Give two ways in which energy is transferred
   a to your body, warming you   b from your body, cooling you

2 Why does your skin go red when you are hot, and blue when you are cold?

3 Explain the role of temperature receptors in the brain.

4 Your skin may feel cool to someone else when you come in from the cold. Does this mean your body core temperature has fallen? Explain your answer.

Key words

vasodilation
vasoconstriction
temperature receptors

35

Behaviour and temperature regulation

Vasoconstriction, vasodilation, sweating, and shivering are automatic responses of the body to temperature changes.

But we also respond by changing our behaviour when we are getting too hot or too cold. The table shows some examples.

Too hot?	Too cold?
Cold food or drinks You are cooled as energy from your body heats the cold food and drink.	**Warm food or drinks** Energy is transferred from the warm food or drink to your body.
Protective clothing Hats, sun umbrellas, and protective clothing reduce the heating effect of the Sun.	**Put on warm clothes** Clothes and hair trap an insulating layer of air. This slows the transfer of energy from your body to the surroundings.
Fan Moving air across the skin can speed up evaporation of sweat, increasing cooling effect.	**Heater** If you move to an area that is warmer than your body, e.g. by a heater or into the Sun, energy will be transferred from the surroundings to your body.

When the body core temperature is not normal

Normal human body core temperature is 36.5–37.5 °C.

Sometimes the body's temperature control system does not work properly, and the body core temperature rises or falls outside the normal range.

- In **pyrexia** (fever) the temperature is higher than 37.5 °C, for example because of infection or heat stroke. In **hyperthermia** it is much higher than normal (above 41 °C).
- In **hypothermia** the body core temperature falls below normal, perhaps because of prolonged exposure to cold and wet conditions.

Questions

1 What does 'normal body core temperature' mean?

2 Give a term used to describe

  a a raised body core temperature

  b a lowered body core temperature

3 Give one possible cause of

  a a raised body core temperature

  b a lowered body core temperature

Key words

pyrexia

hyperthermia

hypothermia

The female reproductive system

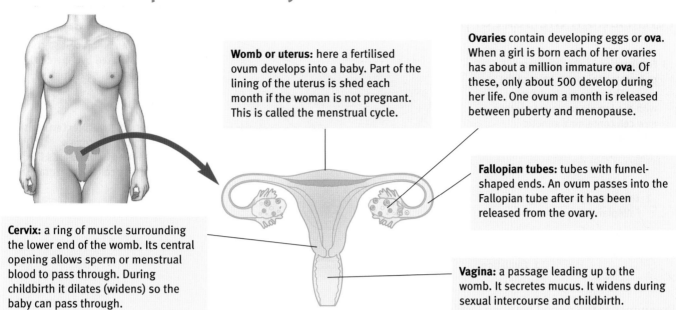

Womb or uterus: here a fertilised ovum develops into a baby. Part of the lining of the uterus is shed each month if the woman is not pregnant. This is called the menstrual cycle.

Ovaries contain developing eggs or **ova**. When a girl is born each of her ovaries has about a million immature **ova**. Of these, only about 500 develop during her life. One ovum a month is released between puberty and menopause.

Fallopian tubes: tubes with funnel-shaped ends. An ovum passes into the Fallopian tube after it has been released from the ovary.

Cervix: a ring of muscle surrounding the lower end of the womb. Its central opening allows sperm or menstrual blood to pass through. During childbirth it dilates (widens) so the baby can pass through.

Vagina: a passage leading up to the womb. It secretes mucus. It widens during sexual intercourse and childbirth.

Human **reproductive systems** have one main function: to produce babies.

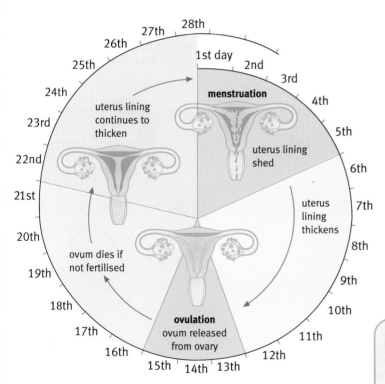

The **menstrual cycle** is controlled by **hormones** carried in the blood. Menstruation starts at puberty and stops between 45 and 55 years old, when a woman can no longer have children. This time in her life is the menopause.

Key words

reproductive system
cervix
womb (uterus)
ovaries
ovum (ova)
Fallopian tubes
vagina
menstrual cycle
hormones
menstruation
ovulation

Questions

1 Describe the journey of an ovum after being released from the ovary if a woman is not pregnant.

2 **a** What is ovulation?

   b Approximately how many days after the start of menstruation does ovulation usually happen?

Pregnancy and birth

Fertilisation: the start of pregnancy

3 Fertilisation: a single sperm penetrates the outer layer of the ovum. The male nucleus fuses with the female nucleus to form a new cell containing genetic information from both parents.

4 During the first 8 weeks the unborn child is called an **embryo**. It starts as a ball of cells formed by repeated division of the fertilised ovum.

5 About 10 days after fertilisation the embryo becomes embedded in the uterus lining, a process called **implantation**.

2 The ovum moves along the Fallopian tube.

1 Ovulation

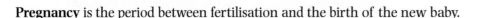

Pregnancy is the period between fertilisation and the birth of the new baby.

First trimester (0–3 months)

The fetus's toes and fingers are distinct with tiny nails, but may still be joined by webs of skin. External ears, eyelids, and teeth buds have formed. The fetus is recognisable as a human being.

The mother's breasts become tender and enlarge. The area around the nipples darkens. Morning sickness is common. She begins to gain weight.

Second trimester (3–6 months)

The fetus grows rapidly and moves more vigorously. External genital organs are visible.

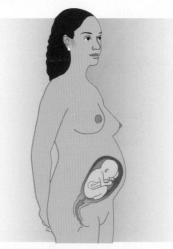

The mother's heart rate increases and her uterus enlarges. From about 20 weeks on, she can usually feel the baby move.

Third trimester (6–9 months)

The fetus becomes increasingly mature. After about week 28, its organs have grown enough so it can just survive with expert care if born prematurely.

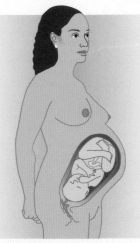

The mother's skin stretches over the abdomen. She feels slight contractions of the uterus, which become more intense as the birth approaches. The enlarged uterus may press on the bladder, increasing the need to urinate. She may feel tired and breathless. Back pain and heartburn are common.

Key words

fertilisation	pregnancy	placenta
embryo	fetus	amnion
implantation	umbilical cord	amniotic fluid

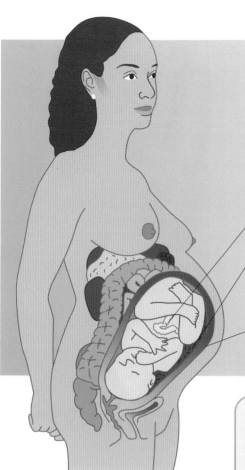

At first the embryo obtains its nutrients and oxygen directly from fluids in the uterus. Later an organ called the placenta forms. Here oxygen and nutrients are exchanged between the mother's blood and the developing baby's blood.

From eight weeks until birth, the unborn child is called a **fetus**.

Umbilical cord: connects the fetus to the placenta.

Placenta: this exchanges materials between mother's and baby's blood. Their blood does not mix but materials are exchanged across a thin membrane.

The placenta also produces female hormones which prevent further pregnancies. They also ensure that the uterus grows at the same rate as the baby and that the breasts are ready to produce milk soon after the baby is born.

Amnion: a bag within the uterus filled with **amniotic fluid**. This clear liquid cushions the fetus, protecting it from knocks. The fluid is swallowed by the fetus, absorbed into its bloodstream, and excreted as urine.

Questions

1 What is the difference between an embryo and a fetus?

2 What is the amnion and what are its functions?

3 Make a flow chart showing the process of pregnancy and birth, from fertilisation to the third stage of labour.

Birth

Birth takes place at about 40 weeks. There are three stages of labour, shown below.

First stage
Contractions of the uterus force the baby's head onto the cervix. The cervix dilates to 10 cm and its mucus plug is discharged. The amnion may break so that amniotic fluid escapes from the vagina, known as 'breaking of the waters'.

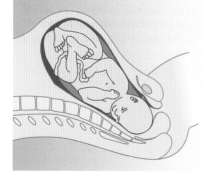

Second stage
Birth contractions become stronger and closer together. The mother feels a strong urge to push with each contraction until the baby is born.

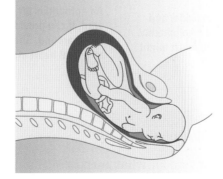

Third stage
Further contractions of the uterus push the placenta and umbilical cord (the 'afterbirth') out of the mother's body.

placenta becoming detached from uterus wall

umbilical cord

Testing the fetus: amniocentesis

Sometimes tests are carried out during pregnancy, to see whether the fetus is developing normally.

In amniocentesis, a sample of amniotic fluid is removed from the uterus for testing. Because there is a small risk to the fetus, an amniocentesis test is not carried out without good reason.

Pain relief during labour

Some mothers experience little pain during childbirth and manage the pain using natural techniques such as relaxation and controlled breathing. For others, drugs such as nitrous oxide (gas and air) or pethidine are needed for pain relief. An epidural is an injection of anaesthetic into the spinal cord.

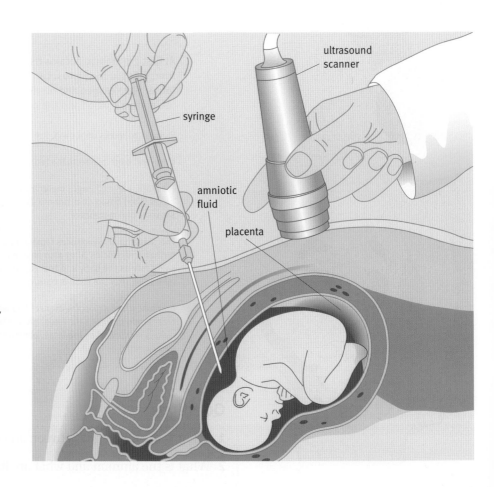

syringe

amniotic fluid

placenta

ultrasound scanner

Gas and air

The woman inhales gas and air through the mask.

tube to cylinder containing mixture of oxygen and nitrous oxide

Gas and air is a mixture of nitrous oxide (dinitrogen oxide) and oxygen. It softens labour pain but does not remove it completely. The woman can control the amount she inhales. Too much might make her feel light-headed and unable to concentrate.

Epidural

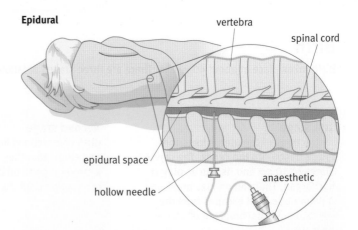

vertebra

spinal cord

epidural space

hollow needle

anaesthetic

An epidural is an injection into the epidural space by the spinal cord. It can provide complete pain relief but the woman cannot move around. She needs a catheter and a drip, and is hooked up to a fetal heart monitor.

Questions

1 What material is tested during an amniocentesis?

2 What drugs may be used during labour, and for what purpose?

The kidneys and urinary system

The **kidneys** have three main functions:

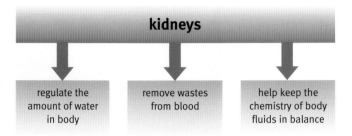

kidneys
regulate the amount of water in body	remove wastes from blood	help keep the chemistry of body fluids in balance

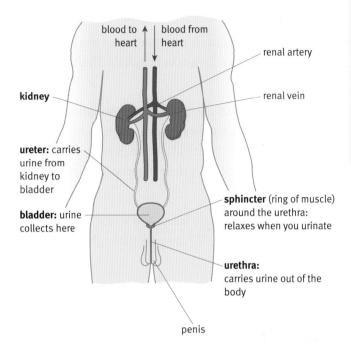

blood to heart — blood from heart

renal artery

renal vein

kidney

ureter: carries urine from kidney to bladder

bladder: urine collects here

sphincter (ring of muscle) around the urethra: relaxes when you urinate

urethra: carries urine out of the body

penis

Blood passes through the kidneys and is filtered. Useful substances such as protein and glucose are retained in the blood. Excess water and waste leave the body in **urine**.

Urine tests can show what is going on in the body.

- If the hormone **HCG** is present, this is a positive pregnancy test.
- If protein is present, the kidneys may be damaged.
- If glucose is present, the person may have **diabetes**.

Diabetes

People with diabetes cannot control the amount of glucose in the blood. After eating carbohydrates the level of glucose in the blood rises dramatically, and the kidneys cannot cope. Glucose leaves the body in the urine.

Some diabetic people can manage their condition with careful control of the diet. They have to avoid eating too much carbohydrate. Others need to inject themselves with the hormone **insulin**, which removes glucose from the blood.

Questions

1 What are the functions of the kidneys?

2 Name two substances that normally remain in the blood after filtration in the kidneys.

3 a Why do diabetics excrete glucose in the urine?

  b What effect does insulin have on the blood?

Key words

kidneys
ureter
bladder
sphincter
urethra
urine
HCG
diabetes
insulin

Imaging: X-rays

Doctors use several imaging techniques to find out what is going on inside the body without harming the patient.

X-rays are used to check whether bones are broken (fractured). **Radiographers** take X-rays in hospitals. Dentists use X-rays to check for cavities in teeth.

X-rays are a form of electromagnetic radiation, like visible light but more energetic. They can pass easily through most body tissues but are absorbed by dense tissues like bone. Sometimes the patient is injected with a dense dye, so that their blood vessels or other body parts show up in the X-rays.

An X-ray image appears black and white. The black parts are body tissue that has let the X-rays pass through. White parts show bone and other dense tissues.

Only a small dose of radiation is needed to make a good image. Radiographers are exposed to higher doses, so they leave the room while the X-ray is being taken. A fetus is very sensitive to X-radiation, so a pregnant women is not X-rayed unless absolutely necessary.

CT scans

CT scanning is a special form of radiography. CT stands for computed axial tomography. X-rays rotate around the patient, and a computer records how much radiation is absorbed. A series of cross-sectional images (slices) is built up.

CT scans may be used to detect

- fractures in the skull
- bleeding in the brain

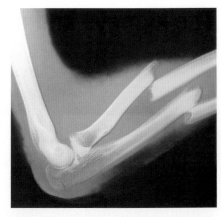

This radiograph shows a broken arm – two bones have been fractured.

shadow cast by the key

metal absorbs X-rays

window

X-ray tube

X-rays from a point source

lead shielding

screen darkens where X-rays reach it

The person being X-rayed stands between the X-ray machine and a sensitive screen. Their bones cast a shadow on the screen, just like this key.

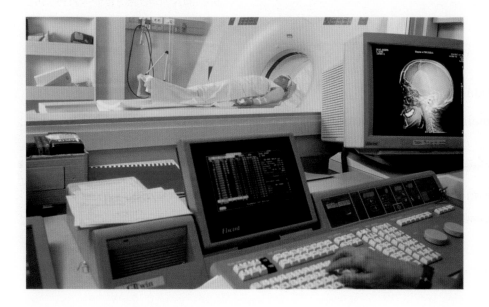

In a CT scanner, the X-ray tube moves around the patient. The images are shown on the computer screen. The surface view of the skull is used to plan where the slices will be taken.

Imaging: MRI

MRI stands for **magnetic resonance imaging**. It is a painless but noisy process that uses radio waves rather than X-rays. Because it does not use X-rays, MRI is safer than CT scanning.

MRI can produce images of every part of the body including bones, joints, blood vessels, and organs. MRI images show more detail of the different body tissues than CT images made using X-rays. They are used to detect problems with nerves, muscles, tendons, and body fluids.

The MRI scanner contains a powerful magnet and sends out radio waves. These penetrate the body, hitting hydrogen atoms which absorb them. The hydrogen atoms then give off radio waves which are detected by the scanner. The computer turns the information they carry into a picture.

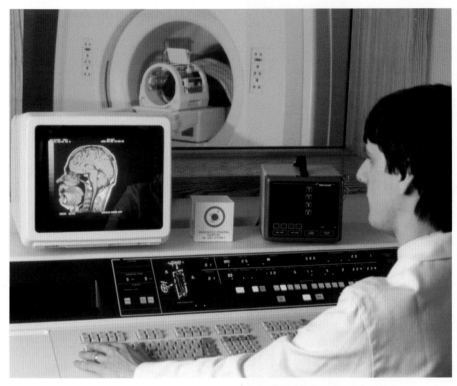

As with CT scanning, to take an MRI the patient lies down and moves through a cylindrical scanner.

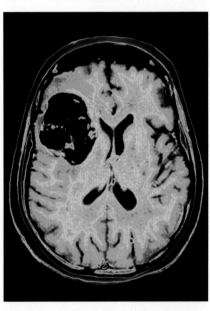

This is an MRI image of a patient's brain. The thick outer layer is the skull. The dark patch (upper left) is a brain tumour.

Questions

1 Why do doctors use imaging techniques?

2 Explain why bones show up white on an X-ray.

3 Name the two bones that are broken in the X-ray on page 42.

4 Give two uses each for

   a CT scanning   **b** MRI scanning

Key words

radiographer

computed axial tomography (CT) scanning

magnetic resonance imaging (MRI)

Imaging: PET

PET is **positron emission tomography**, a relatively recent development. PET scans provide information about how well different organs of the body are working. For example, they can identify cancerous tumours.

A radioactive chemical combined with a sugar is injected into the patient's bloodstream up to an hour before the scan. This chemical moves through the body and is absorbed by different tissues.

Different colours in the scan show different levels of absorption. Cancerous cells grow and divide more rapidly than healthy cells, so cancerous tissue absorbs the chemical more than normal tissue.

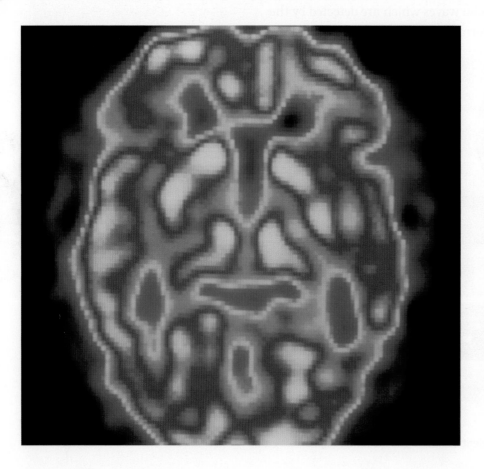

A PET scan of the brain. The different colours show areas that have absorbed different amounts of chemical.

Questions

1 Look at the MRI image on page 43. Why does this scan show the tumour better than a CT scan would?

2 Why is MRI less dangerous than CT scanning?

3 How is a patient prepared for a PET scan?

4 Why do active cells take up the radioactive chemical more than normal cells?

Imaging: ultrasound scanning

Ultrasound scanning uses sound waves to make an image of the inside of the body. The technique is also known as **sonography**. The GP may refer a patient for an ultrasound scan if they have an unexplained lump, for example.

The sonographer spreads a gel on the patient's skin and moves a scanner over the skin surface. The scanner sends very high frequency sound waves through the body. Where the waves meet boundaries between different tissues, such as between muscle and fatty tissue, they are reflected in a particular way.

The scanner picks up these reflected waves and a computer turns the signals into a picture. The sonographer can see the heart beating and the arteries expanding rhythmically. They can recognise organs such as the liver, kidneys, and pancreas on the black and white image. The scan will reveal whether the organs appear normal, or whether further investigation is needed.

As well as taking images externally, small ultrasound probes can be placed into body openings such as the mouth, ear, or vagina, to get a clearer picture.

X-rays can harm a developing fetus, but ultrasound waves are much safer. So ultrasound scans are carried out on pregnant women to check the fetus is developing normally.

The scanner is moved over the skin. Without the gel, air gaps would spoil the image.

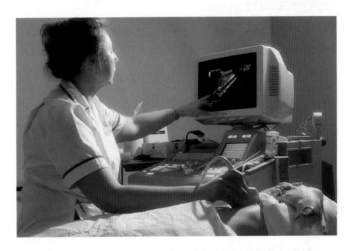

The sonographer can see the blood vessels. Turning the scanner round gives a different view.

Questions

1 What type of waves does ultrasound use?

2 Why is ultrasound the imaging method used for pregnant women?

3 Make a table or diagram to compare the following imaging techniques: X-rays, CT scans, MRI, PET, and ultrasound scanning. Include one medical use of each method.

Key words

positron emission tomography (PET)
ultrasound scanning
sonography

Procedures and techniques

Measuring body temperature

➡ Equipment

Several devices are used to measure **body core temperature**. Two are shown here.

In a clinical thermometer the mercury expands as the temperature goes up, and rises up a glass tube. The tube is **calibrated** to show the temperature.

A digital thermometer has a probe connected to an electronic display.

A liquid crystal thermometer measures skin temperature. It changes colour to show the temperature.

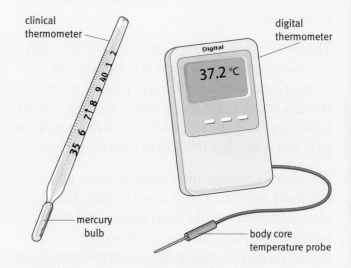

➡ Procedure

Approximate body core temperatures can be taken by placing the mercury bulb or temperature probe

- ▶ in the mouth, under the tongue
- ▶ under the arm in the armpit
- ▶ with a special probe in the ear

More accurate body core temperatures are taken with a probe placed in the **oesophagus** or the **rectum**.

The thermometer must be calibrated to give reliable readings. Shake a clinical thermometer to return the mercury to the bulb.

Always use the same body site to monitor body temperature, as temperature varies over the body.

Record the body temperature in **degrees Celsius** (°C).

➡ Interpreting the reading

The normal range of body core temperature is between 36 and 37.5 °C. Children have slightly higher temperatures due to their higher **metabolic rate**.

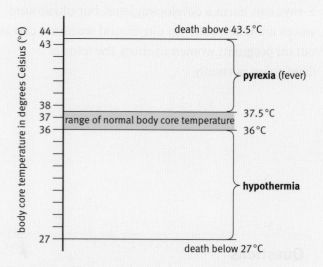

The range of body core temperatures people can survive

Measuring pulse rate

⊕ Equipment

▸ wristwatch with a second hand

⊕ Interpreting the reading

▸ Healthy adults have a pulse rate of 60–100 beats per minute.

▸ Infants and children have much higher pulse rates.

▸ The pulse rate increases during exercise, panic attack, anxiety, or if the person has a heart disorder.

▸ A weak pulse may be a sign of low blood pressure, shock, or a heart disorder.

▸ A low pulse rate can result from illness. Fit athletes also have low pulse rates, as their heart and lungs work efficiently.

⊕ Procedure

The pulse can be **palpated** (felt) where you can press an artery near the body surface against a firm structure such as bone. The diagram opposite shows some places where you can feel the pulse. It is usually taken in the radial artery.

The person should be relaxed.

1 Place your first and second fingers along the radial artery and press gently against the bone.

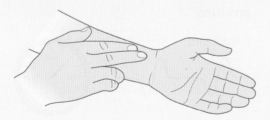

2 Apply enough pressure to feel the pulse but not so much that the artery is blocked.

3 Count the number of pulses in 60 seconds. This gives the pulse rate in beats per minute.

An electronic pulse monitor may be used in place of this manual procedure.

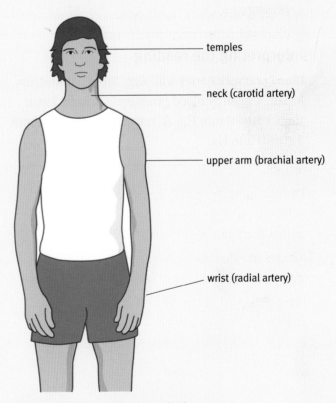

temples

neck (carotid artery)

upper arm (brachial artery)

wrist (radial artery)

Major pulse points of the upper body

Measuring blood pressure

→ Equipment

Blood pressure is measured using a manual or electronic **sphygmomanometer**. This consists of

- an inflatable sleeve or cuff
- a means of inflating the cuff (by squeezing a rubber bulb, or with compressed air)
- a device for measuring the pressure in the cuff

→ The reading

- Blood pressure is measured in **millimetres of mercury (mm Hg)**.
- There are two numbers, e.g. 130/80 mm Hg ('130 over 80').
- The first figure is higher. This is the **systolic blood pressure**.
- The second, lower figure is the **diastolic blood pressure**.

→ Interpreting the reading

Blood pressure varies with age, fitness, and stress levels. A healthy blood pressure is usually lower than 140/90 mm Hg. A 'normal' reading is about 120/80 mm Hg.

→ Procedure

Here is the manual procedure. An electronic sphygmomanometer takes readings automatically.

1 Place the cuff around the upper arm. Hold a stethoscope to the brachial artery just below the cuff. Listen for the pulse.

2 Inflate the cuff until you can no longer hear the pulse.

no pulse heard

3 Slowly deflate the cuff until you hear the pulse start again. Record the reading as the systolic pressure.

pulse heard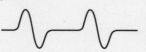

4 Deflate the cuff further. The pulse sound will suddenly die away. When it starts to die away, record the reading as the diastolic pressure.

no pulse heard

Measuring breathing rate

The **breathing rate** is measured by timing the number of breaths in one minute. One complete breath is an inhalation, an exhalation, and the pause that follows.

⮂ Equipment

▸ wristwatch with a second hand

⮂ Procedure

1 Observe the depth and pattern of breathing. Describe the depth of breathing as normal, shallow, or deep.

2 Count the number of breaths for 30 seconds, by watching the rise and fall of the chest wall. If you see any abnormality in breathing, then count for at least one minute. The person should be unaware that you are counting their breaths.

3 Calculate the breathing rate in breaths per minute:

breaths per minute = breaths counted in 30 seconds × 2

⮂ Interpreting the reading

Normal breathing rates vary with age.

▸ infants: 30 or more breaths per minute

▸ children: 22–28 breaths per minute

▸ adolescents: 18–22 breaths per minute

▸ healthy adults: 14–20 breaths per minute

A normal breathing pattern is evenly paced and automatic. It should appear effortless.

Measuring the body mass index

The **body mass index** (BMI) is found by dividing the body mass in kilograms by the square of the height in metres:

$$BMI = \frac{\text{body mass in kg}}{(\text{height in m})^2}$$

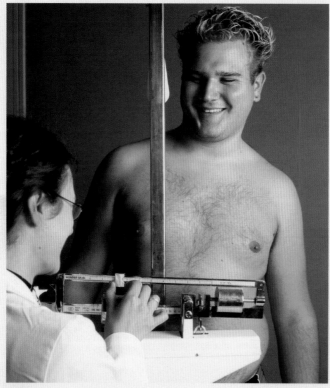

This man is being weighed and measured so that his body mass index can be calculated.

This index is used to estimate whether a person's body weight is at a desirable level, or too high, or too low.

Equipment

- stadiometer or accurate weight scales and height rule

Procedures

Measuring body mass

- Use scales on a hard, flat, uncarpeted floor.
- The person should wear light clothing and no shoes.
- Record mass in kilograms to one decimal point.

Measuring body height

- Ideally, use a stadiometer. This combines a weight scale with a height measurer.
- The person should stand tall, facing forwards.
- Mark the measurement at the highest point of the head.
- Record the height in metres to one decimal point.

Calculating BMI

Calculate the BMI using the formula:

$$BMI = \frac{\text{body mass in kg}}{(\text{height in m})^2}$$

Interpreting the result

Most authorities use the following guidelines:

BMI	Condition	Advice given
under 20	underweight	may need to gain weight
20.0–24.9	advisable range	
25.0–29.9	overweight	some weight loss may be beneficial to health
30.0–34.9	obese	need to lose weight
35 and over	severely obese	urgent need to lose weight; consult a doctor

Being overweight (BMI over 27) leads to increased health risks such as high blood pressure and diabetes. The risk gradually increases as the BMI rises further. With a BMI over 35, the risk of premature death is doubled.

Taking skinfold measurements

⊙ Equipment

 ▸ skinfold calipers

⊙ Procedure

 ▸ Take all measurements on the same side of the body.

 ▸ The skin should be dry and free of oils or lotions.

 ▸ Do not take skinfold measurements on obese people, women who are menstruating, or people who have recently been exercising.

1 Carefully identify and mark the skinfold sites: triceps, scapula, abdomen. Measure them in this order.

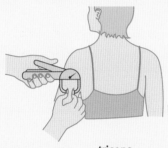
triceps

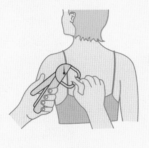
scapula

abdomen

2 Hold the calipers in one hand. Take a double layer of skin with the thumb and index finger of the other hand. Start with your thumb and finger about 7 cm apart, then gently pull the skinfold away from the body.

3 Place the caliper head half-way down the fold.

4 Depending on the type of caliper, release the trigger or apply steady pressure, firm but not uncomfortable.

5 Maintain the pinch and read the dial within 3–4 seconds after applying the pressure.

6 Take a measurement at each site, then take repeat readings in the same order.

7 Re-measure if the first and second readings at a site are not within 1–2 mm (or 10%).

8 For each site, record the average of the two nearest readings. Then add together the average skinfold measurements from the three sites.

⊙ Interpreting the results

The rating chart below gives the amount of body fat (excellent = low body fat).

Sum of skinfold thickness in millimetres		Rating
Males	**Females**	
less than 22	less than 25	excellent
22–34	25–42	good
35–73	43–65	average
74–90	66–82	fair
greater than 90	greater than 82	poor

Performing a step test

Step tests are designed to assess **aerobic fitness**.

⮎ Equipment

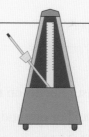

- ▸ a step or bench no more than 50 cm high
- ▸ a stopwatch
- ▸ a metronome

⮎ Procedure

First complete a physical activity readiness questionnaire (PAR-Q). If you have any medical problems do not do a step test without a doctor's approval.

1 Set the metronome at 2 beats per second.

2 Start the stopwatch and step in time to the beat:
  1 first foot up
  2 second foot up
  3 first foot down
  4 second foot down
  1 first foot up . . .

3 Repeat for 5 minutes or until you are too tired to continue. Do not stop the stopwatch.

4 Sit down immediately you stop. Note the time.

5 Take your pulse rate (see page 47) exactly 1, 2, and 3 minutes after you stop.

⮎ Interpreting the results

Calculate your step test score:

- ▸ time you stepped for in seconds × 100 (A)
- ▸ add up the three pulse rates, then multiply by 2 (B)
- ▸ step test score = $\dfrac{A}{B}$

The higher the score, the more aerobically fit you are.

Male score	Female score	Guideline for 16-year-olds
over 90	over 86	excellent
80–90	76–86	above average
65–79	61–75	average
55–64	50–60	below average
below 55	below 50	poor

⮎ Example

A subject stepped for 3 minutes, with pulse rates 65, 50, and 35:

- ▸ A is 3 × 60 × 100 = 18 000
- ▸ B is 65 + 50 + 35 = 150
- ▸ Step test score = $\dfrac{18\ 000}{300} = 60$

Preparing a blood slide

⮕ Equipment

▶ two microscope slides

▶ blood (use ink to practise the technique, or animal blood as supplied) with dropper

⮕ Procedure

1 Place a small drop of blood on a clean slide.

2 Hold a second clean slide at an angle to the first one.

CHECK SAFETY
Never work unsupervised

▶ Do not take a sample of your own blood.

▶ Take care with glass slides.

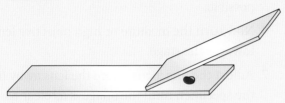

3 Make sure the slides are touching. Pull the top slide back to touch the drop. The drop will start to spread.

4 Keep the slides firmly touching. Push the top slide away in one smooth motion to produce a smear. It should be thin at one end and thicker near the original drop of blood.

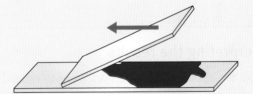

⮕ Interpreting the results

Examine the blood slide under a microscope (see page 54).

Blood slides give information such as

▶ number of red blood cells (red cell count)

▶ proportion of red to white blood cells

▶ number of reticulocytes (immature red blood cells with nucleus)

▶ deficiency anaemia (few red blood cells)

▶ sickle-cell anaemia (sickle-shaped red blood cells)

Using a microscope

⇨ Equipment

▶ light microscope

▶ slide for viewing (the specimen)

CHECK SAFETY
Never work unsupervised

▶ Never look down a microscope without a slide on the stage.

▶ Do not use a microscope in direct sunlight.

▶ Always start with the objective lens near the slide and move it away so that you do not smash the slide.

⇨ Procedure

1 Switch on the light or adjust the mirror so it shines light through the specimen.

2 Turn the smallest objective lens towards the stage. Rotate the turret until you hear a click.

3 Clip the slide on the stage.

4 Look down the eyepiece lens with one eye. Try and keep the other eye open.

5 Adjust the coarse focus. Move the lens away from the specimen until the image is as clear as possible.

6 Now turn the medium or high objective lens towards the stage.

7 Adjust the fine focus. Move the lens away from the specimen until the image is as clear as possible.

⇨ Interpreting the results

Make a clear labelled pencil drawing to record your observations.

Include the total magnification. To calculate this:

$$\text{magnification of microscope} = \text{magnification of eyepiece lens} \times \text{magnification of objective lens}$$

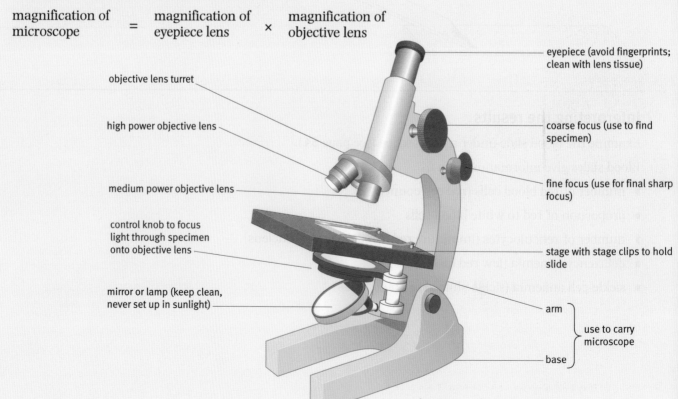

objective lens turret

high power objective lens

medium power objective lens

control knob to focus light through specimen onto objective lens

mirror or lamp (keep clean, never set up in sunlight)

eyepiece (avoid fingerprints; clean with lens tissue)

coarse focus (use to find specimen)

fine focus (use for final sharp focus)

stage with stage clips to hold slide

arm

use to carry microscope

base

Testing urine and other body products

❯ Procedure

❯ Collecting the specimen

- A sample of urine is usually collected in a sterile container, first thing in the morning.
- To avoid contamination with bacteria, an antiseptic wipe may be used around the urethra first.

❯ Testing

1. Dip a test strip in the urine for a standard time, according to the manufacturer's instructions.
2. Compare the colour of the strip to the colours on a chart.

Tests available include

- the amount of glucose in the urine
- protein or blood in the urine
- whether a woman is pregnant

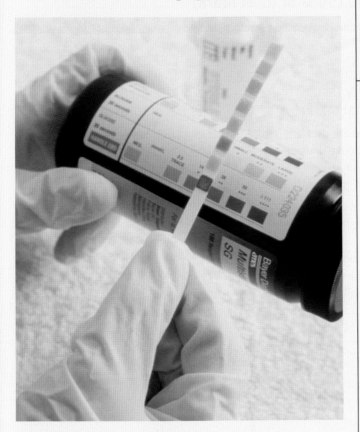

This multiple test stick tests urine for several substances including glucose, protein, and blood.

❯ Interpreting the reading

- Glucose present may be a sign of diabetes.
- Protein present may be a sign of kidney damage or disease.
- Blood present may be a sign of disease in the kidney, urinary system, or bladder.

The results are usually reported to the patient's GP.

❯ Testing other body products

Saliva can be collected in a cotton bud and tested for antibodies that indicate the start of an infection.

Pus is the thick fluid found in inflamed areas such as abscesses or ulcers. Analysing a pus sample shows which bacteria are present.

The colour and consistency of **faeces** aid the diagnosis of a range of diseases. A red colour may indicate the presence of blood, a sign of bleeding in the gut.

Your Work-related portfolio

The Additional Applied Science course aims to help you

- carry out specific scientific proceedures where the results matter
- apply science knowledge and techniques, to solve problems
- learn about a variety of science-based workplaces
- select, organise, and communicate information clearly and logically

You will show your progress with these skills through your Work-related portfolio.

Your Work-related portfolio counts for 50% of the total mark. Your school or college will give you details of the marking scheme for each part of it. This will help you check that your work meets the criteria for success.

Across the three modules that you study, the Work-related portfolio requires

- six Standard procedures (two from each module)
- one Suitability test (from any module)
- one Work-related report

Work-related portfolio (50% of total mark)

Standard procedures
(6 × 2% = 12% of total mark)

A standard procedure is a series of practical steps, often including scientific techniques, that will achieve the same result no matter who carries it out. It involves following instructions, working safely, and making measurements or observations carefully. You will carry out six, each counting for 2%.

Suitability test
(21% of total mark)

Suitability tests are another example of how science is used in the workplace. There are three types of test you might carry out:

- testing a material or comparing materials for a particular purpose
- comparing different procedures used for the same purpose
- testing the suitability of a device for a particular purpose

Work-related report
(17% of total mark)

This gives you the opportunity to find out about some science-related activity carried out in a real workplace, such as a hospital or factory. You present your findings in a Work-related report. Choose your topic carefully, and don't let your report become too large. A good topic will

- interest you
- contain enough scientific content
- have information sources which you can identify, obtain, and understand

Standard procedures

Typically Standard procedures will be carried out and assessed in a single lesson. They will involve a series of steps. Your teacher will tell you what, if anything, needs to be recorded.

Suitability test

You will need to

- describe desirable properties or characteristics
- follow or devise a suitable approach
- collect reliable data
- evaluate the suitability of the material, procedure, or device
- communicate through a structured report

Work-related report

For your Work-related report, you will probably use the following sources of information:

- Internet
- school library
- local public library
- TV/video
- newspapers and magazines
- museums and exhibitions

You may also gather information from specific people or organisations:

- interview a practitioner (possibly a family member or a friend)
- write a letter to an organisation
- telephone to request a leaflet, or to find out who to write to

To obtain useful information from any of these, you will need to prepare detailed questions in advance. Speak (or write) politely and explain who you are and what you are doing.

Use all information sources selectively, picking out parts relevant to your topic and writing in your own words. Keep a detailed record of any information sources you use.

Tip

The best advice is 'plan ahead'. Give your work the time it needs and work steadily and evenly over the time you are given. Your deadlines will come all too quickly, especially as you will have coursework to do in other subjects.

Life care organisations

British Heart Foundation (BHF) — A UK charity that funds research and education in the fight against heart disease.

Exercise Referral Scheme — A scheme in which doctors can refer patients for a course of exercise with a fitness instructor.

Fitness Industry Association (FIA) — An organisation that sets standards for health and gym clubs.

Food Advertising Unit (FAU) — A centre for information, communication, and research in the area of food advertising.

Food Standards Agency (FSA) — An independent watchdog organisation that works to protect public health and consumer interests in relation to food safety.

Health Protection Agency — An independent health authority within the NHS which protects public health.

National Blood Service — The part of the NHS that supplies blood.

National Health Service (NHS) — The organisation that provides health care in the UK. There are separate branches of the NHS for England, Wales, Scotland, and Northern Ireland.

NHS Direct — A telephone and Internet service for advice on health problems.

Register of Exercise Professionals — The professional body for fitness instructors and other professionals who work in the field of exercise.

World Health Organization (WHO) — The United Nations agency for health.

Glossary

aerobic exercise Any exercise of moderate to low intensity that involves large groups of muscles and increases the body's demand for oxygen. Aerobic exercise includes cycling, running, and swimming.

aerobic fitness The ability to keep exercising at low to moderate intensity.

airways Parts of the body through which air enters and leaves the lungs.

alveolus (plural **alveoli**) One of many tiny air-filled sacs at the end of each bronchiole through which gases are exchanged in the lungs.

amnion A membrane that encloses the fetus as it develops in the womb.

amniotic fluid A fluid which fills the space in the womb where the fetus develops. Amniotic fluid protects the fetus from drying out, and cushions it against injury.

anaemia A condition in which either the amount of haemoglobin in blood, or the number of red blood cells, is lower than normal. The person is pale and feels tired.

antioxidants Chemicals that 'mop up' the products of metabolism that can damage the body.

arteries Blood vessels that carry blood from the heart to the rest of the body.

atrium (plural **atria**) One of the upper chambers of the heart. The two atria pump blood to the ventricles.

basal metabolic rate The rate at which all the chemical reactions take place in a person at complete rest and at a comfortable temperature. The basal metabolic rate (BMR) refers to the minimum amount of energy needed to keep the person alive.

bladder A muscular sac which stores urine passed from the kidneys.

blood pressure Pressure (force per unit area) exerted by blood on the walls of a blood vessel. It is usually expressed as two figures: systolic blood pressure over diastolic blood pressure, e.g. 120/80 mm Hg.

body core temperature Temperature in the part of the body containing the vital organs (the brain, heart, lungs, and kidneys).

body mass index (BMI) An estimate of body composition based on a weight to height ratio.

breathing rate The number of breaths taken in a given time, usually per minute.

bronchioles Small air tubules leading off from the bronchi.

bronchus (plural **bronchi**) Tube leading from the windpipe (trachea) to the right or left lung.

calibrated A measuring instrument is calibrated when its accuracy is checked.

cancer A general term used to describe a malignant growth in body tissue. Cancer is caused when cells divide in an abnormal or uncontrolled way.

capillaries Narrow blood vessels between arteries and veins. Capillaries have very thin walls, only one cell thick. This allows gases, nutrients, and waste products to be exchanged between blood and tissues.

cardiovascular disease A disease of the heart and blood vessels.

cardiovascular system The organ system that circulates blood round the body. It consists of the heart and blood vessels.

cartilage A connective tissue that is tough and flexible. Cartilage is found at the ends of bones, in joints, in the nose, and in the external ear.

cervix The opening of the uterus that projects into the vagina. The cervix dilates during childbirth.

computed (axial) tomography (CT or **CAT scanning)** A form of radiography that uses computer technology to make layers of images of a part of the body. It produces very clear X-ray images of internal body structures.

coronary arteries The blood vessels that supply the heart.

coronary heart disease A malfunction of the heart caused by a blockage in one or more of the arteries supplying blood to the heart.

degrees Celsius (°C) Units used to measure temperature. 0 °C is the temperature at which water freezes and 100 °C is the temperature at which water boils.

diabetes A disease in which there is excessive excretion of urine. The body cannot control the blood glucose level.

diaphragm A muscular sheet of tissue that separates the chest cavity from the abdomen.

diastolic blood pressure The blood pressure when all parts of the heart muscle are relaxed and the heart is filling with blood.

electrocardiogram (ECG) A graph showing electrical events during the heartbeat. It can be used to reveal irregular heartbeats or damage to heart muscle.

embryo A fertilised egg in its very early stages before human characteristics appear.

emphysema A disease in which the tissues of the airways lose elasticity. The alveoli walls break down, reducing the surface area for gas exchange and causing breathlessness.

evaporation The process of liquid turning to vapour below its boiling point. The evaporation of sweat is the body's main cooling system during exercise.

faeces Body waste made up of bile, undigested food, bacteria, and mucus.

Fallopian tubes The tubes that carry an egg from the ovary to the uterus.

fertilisation The point at which a male sex cell (sperm) fuses with a female sex cell (ovum).

fetus A human embryo once human features become recognisable. This occurs at about 8 weeks into pregnancy.

gas exchange The exchange of oxygen and carbon dioxide that takes place in the lungs..

general practitioner (GP) A qualified doctor who is also the first point of contact with the National Health Service for most people. A GP provides a range of care within the local community.

haemoglobin The protein molecule in red blood cells. Haemoglobin gives blood its red colour and transports oxygen round the body.

HCG A hormone secreted by the placenta during pregnancy.

hormones Chemicals that are produced in one part of the body, but carried to another part where they have a specific effect.

hyperthermia A very high core body temperature.

hypothermia An abnormally low body core temperature, below 36 °C.

implantation A fertilised egg becomes embedded into the lining of the uterus.

insulin A hormone secreted in the pancreas. Insulin is released into the bloodstream when blood glucose levels rise. It then stimulates the liver, muscle, and fat cells to remove glucose from blood, and to store it as glycogen and fat.

intercostal muscles A set of muscles between the ribs. The intercostal muscles contract during breathing to draw air into the lungs as you breathe in, and force air out as you breathe out.

joint A point of contact between two or more bones.

kidneys Organs that remove wastes from the body, and regulate the levels of water and salts in the body.

ligament Connective tissue that joins two bones together.

lungs A pair of organs in the chest cavity. They have a large surface area because of their millions of alveoli and so allow gaseous exchange to take place. The lungs are linked to the air by a system of tubes, the airways.

magnetic resonance imaging (MRI) A technique that uses radio waves to produce images of internal soft structures such as muscles and tendons.

menstrual cycle The cycle of changes in a woman's body associated with ovulation. The cycle takes approximately 28 days.

menstruation The shedding of the uterus lining each month as part of the menstrual cycle.

metabolic rate The rate at which all the chemical reactions in the body take place.

millimetres of mercury (mm Hg) Units used to measure blood pressure.

muscle An organ that contracts to allow movement in the body.

obese Term used to describe somebody with excessive fat stored in the body.

ovaries A pair of organs in a woman that produce eggs.

ovulation The release of an egg from an ovary, ready for fertilisation.

ovum (plural ova) An egg: the female reproductive cell.

palpated Examined using the sense of touch (felt).

physcial activity level (PAL) A way of measuring how much exercise people do each day. PAL is total energy required over 24 hours divided by basal metabolic rate over 24 hours.

placenta A spongy structure that attaches an embryo or fetus to the uterus wall of the mother during pregnancy. Nutrients and gases are exchanged between the fetus and mother through the placenta.

plasma A clear straw-coloured and fluid component of blood.

platelets Cell fragments found in blood. Platelets play a role in clotting.

positron emission tomography (PET) A technique in which isotopes are injected into the bloodstream. Their movement through the body can be followed using an external camera. PET can be used to study the activity of muscle and brain tissue.

pregnancy The period of time from the fertilisation of an egg to the birth of a baby.

primary health care Care provided within the community at the first point of contact with a health team.

pulse The rhythmic expansion of the arteries, coinciding with the contraction of the left ventricle of the heart.

pus The result of inflammation caused by bacteria. Pus is a thick, yellowy substance made up of dead white blood cells and bacteria, broken cells, and tissue fluid.

pyrexia Fever, a condition in which the core body temperature has risen to over 37.5 °C.

radiographer A person who takes photographic images of body structures using X-rays.

red blood cells Blood cells containing haemoglobin. In humans, they are biconcave discs and have no nucleus.

referral Treatment at a hospital or other institution arranged through a GP.

rehabilitation The process of restoring activity and health to somebody who has been injured or sick.

reproductive system All the organs of the male or female body involved in sexual reproduction.

respiration A process in the body that generates energy from the breakdown of food.

respiratory system All the organs and tissues involved in breathing and gas exchange. The respiratory system includes the nose and nasal passages, the pharynx, the windpipe (trachea), the bronchi, and the lungs.

saliva A watery fluid secreted by glands behind the mouth. Saliva contains mucus, salts, and an enzyme called amylase that begins the digestion of starch.

shivering The involuntary contraction of muscles to warm the body.

sickle-cell anaemia A disease in which a large number of red blood cells are sickle shaped and cannot carry oxygen properly.

skeletal muscles Muscles that are attached to the skeleton.

skeleton The bones and other structures that form a framework for the body. The skeleton supports and protects internal organs, and provides a system of levers that allow the body to move. Some parts also make red blood cells.

skinfold measurements Measurements of a fold of body tissue. A skinfold measurement includes skin and the fatty tissue beneath, but no muscle.

sonography Another name for ultrasound scanning.

sphincter A circular muscle that closes an opening when it contracts. Emptying the bladder of urine is controlled by a sphincter muscle.

sphygmomanometer An instrument used for measuring blood pressure in the arteries. It usually consists of an inflatable cuff, a stethoscope, and a pressure gauge.

stadiometer A device with a ruler for measuring height and scales for measuring body mass.

step tests Tests of cardiovascular fitness that involve stepping on and off a bench or chair for a period and then taking a pulse reading. The quicker you return to a resting heart rate, the fitter you are.

stroke An interruption of the blood supply to the brain caused by a blood clot, head injury, or burst blood vessel in the brain.

sweating The secretion of a watery fluid onto the skin. Sweating helps the body to cool down as it evaporates from the skin.

synovial fluid Fluid found in the cavity of a joint. Synovial fluid lubricates and nourishes the joint, and prevents two bones from rubbing against each other.

synovial membrane Loose connective tissue lining the inside of a joint capsule in a synovial (free-moving) joint. It secretes synovial fluid.

systolic blood pressure The blood pressure when blood is pumped from the left ventricle to the rest of the body.

temperature receptors A group of cells that allow the body to detect changes in temperature.

tendon Connective tissue that joins muscle to a bone.

trachea The windpipe which carries air to the lungs.

ultrasound scanning Applying ultrasonic waves (very high frequency sound waves) to examine internal organs. Ultrasound scanning can also be used to treat soft tissue injuries.

umbilical cord A cord made of blood vessels and connective tissue that attaches an embryo or fetus to its placenta. It carries nutrients and oxygen from mother to fetus, and removes waste products.

ureter One of a pair of tubes that carries urine from each of the kidneys to the bladder.

urethra The tube that takes urine from the bladder to the outside.

urine A watery solution of salts and urea produced by the kidneys.

uterus Another name for womb.

vagina In women, the tube that leads from the uterus to the outside.

vasoconstriction Narrowing of blood vessels which reduces blood flow to the area of the body supplied by the blood vessels.

vasodilation Widening of blood vessels which increases blood flow to the area of the body supplied by the blood vessels.

veins Blood vessels that carry blood to the heart.

ventilation The exchange of air between the lungs and the environment, also known as breathing.

ventricle One of the lower chambers of the heart. The right ventricle pumps blood to the lungs. The left ventricle pumps blood to the rest of the body.

white blood cells Blood cells that defend the body against disease.

womb The muscular organ in a woman that holds a developing baby. The uterus nourishes and protects the fetus during pregnancy.

Index

OXFORD
UNIVERSITY PRESS

Great Clarendon Street, Oxford OX2 6DP

Oxford University Press is a department of the University of Oxford.
It furthers the University's objective of excellence in research, scholarship,
and education by publishing worldwide in

Oxford New York

Auckland Cape Town Dar es Salaam Hong Kong Karachi
Kuala Lumpur Madrid Melbourne Mexico City Nairobi
New Delhi Shanghai Taipei Toronto

With offices in

Argentina Austria Brazil Chile Czech Republic France Greece
Guatemala Hungary Italy Japan Poland Portugal Singapore
South Korea Switzerland Thailand Turkey Ukraine Vietnam

© University of York on behalf of UYSEG and the Nuffield Foundation 2006

The moral rights of the authors have been asserted

Database right Oxford University Press (maker)

First published 2006

All rights reserved. No part of this publication may be reproduced,
stored in a retrieval system, or transmitted, in any form or by any means,
without the prior permission in writing of Oxford University Press,
or as expressly permitted by law, or under terms agreed with the appropriate
reprographics rights organization. Enquiries concerning reproduction
outside the scope of the above should be sent to the Rights Department,
Oxford University Press, at the address above

You must not circulate this book in any other binding or cover
and you must impose this same condition on any acquirer

British Library Cataloguing in Publication Data

Data available

ISBN-13: 978-0-19-915026-7
ISBN-10: 0-19-915026-5

10 9 8 7 6 5

Printed in Italy by Rotolito Lombarda

Acknowledgements

Contributors: Ginny Hales, Nigel Heslop

These resources have been developed to support teachers and students
undertaking a new OCR suite of GCSE Science specifications, *Twenty First Century
Science*.

Many people from schools, colleges, universities, industry, and the professions
have contributed to the production of these resources. The feedback from over 75
Pilot Centres was invaluable. It led to significant changes to the course
specifications, and to the supporting resources for teaching and learning.

The University of York Science Education Group (UYSEG) and Nuffield Curriculum
Centre worked in partnership with an OCR team led by Mary Whitehouse,
Elizabeth Herbert and Emily Clare to create the specifications, which have their
origins in the *Beyond 2000* report (Millar & Osborne, 1998) and subsequent Key
Stage 4 development work undertaken by UYSEG and the Nuffield Curriculum
Centre for QCA. Bryan Milner and Michael Reiss also contributed to this work,
which is reported in: *21st Century Science GCSE Pilot Development: Final Report* (UYSEG,
March 2002).

Sponsors
The development of *Twenty First Century Science* was made possible by generous
support from:
• The Nuffield Foundation
• The Salters' Institute
• The Wellcome Trust

The publisher would like to thank the following for their kind permission to
reproduce copyright material:

p2 SportsChrome/Empics; **p3l** BSIP, Laurent/B. Hop Ame/Science Photo Library;
p3r Pictor/ Imagestate/Alamy; **p6** Jerome Yeats/Alamy; **p7** Lester Lefkowitz/
Corbis UK Ltd.; **p8l** ER Productions/Corbis UK Ltd.; **p8r** Sarah Codrington/Nuffield
Foundation; **p9l** Science Photo Library; **p9r** Antonia Reeve/Science Photo Library;
p9t Ed Kashi/Corbis UK Ltd.; **p12b** Oxford University Press; **p13** PhotoDisc;
p14 Adam Hart-Davis/Science Photo Library; **p15** Family Planning Association;
p16l Wang Xiaochuan/Xinhua/Corbis UK Ltd.; **p16r** Kimimasa Mayama/Reuters/
Corbis UK Ltd.; **p18b** Photodisc Blue/Getty Images; **p18** Ronnie Kaufman/Corbis
UK Ltd.; **p19t** Jon Feingersh/Corbis UK Ltd.; **p20t** Ed Bock/Corbis UK Ltd.;
p20b Oxford University Press; **p21l** Manfred Kage/Science Photo Library;
p21r Astrid & Hanns-Frieder Michler/Science Photo Library; **p22** Lester Lefkowitz/
Corbis UK Ltd.; **p29l** Eris Grave/Science Photo Library; **p29c** Dr Gopal Murti/
Science Photo Library; **p29r** Michael Abbey/Science Photo Library; **p30** Firefly
Productions/Corbis UK Ltd.; **p31tl** John Burbidge/Science Photo Library;
p31cr Biophoto Associates/Science Photo Library; **p31b** Science Photo Library;
p32 W.G. Willis/Oxford Scientific Films/photolibrary.com; **p42t** Dept. Of Clinical
Radiology, Salisbury District Hospital/Science Photo Library; **p42b** Bsip Edwige/
Science Photo Library; **p43l** Simon Fraser/Dept. Of Neuroradiology, Newcastle
General Hospital/Science Photo Library; **p43r** Zephyr/Science Photo Library;
p44t Michael Donne/Science Photo Library; **p44** Tim Beddow/Science Photo
Library; **p50** Mauro Fermariello/Science Photo Library; **p56** Faye Norman/Science
Photo Library; **cover** Steve Allen/Brand X Pictures/Alamy

Illustrations by IFA Design, Plymouth, UK and Clive Goodyer